JANE'S POCKET BOOK OF MAJOR COMBAT AIRCRAFT

JANE'S POCKET BOOK OF MAJOR COMBAT AIRCRAFT

Compiled by MICHAEL J. H. TAYLOR and KENNETH MUNSON
Edited by JOHN W. R. TAYLOR, FRHistS, AFRAeS, FSLAET

COLLIER BOOKS
A Division of Macmillan Publishing Co., Inc.
New York

Macmillan Publishing Co., Inc.
866 Third Avenue, New York, N.Y. 10022
Collier Macmillan Canada, Inc.

Library of Congress Catalog Card Number: 73-9331

ISBN 0-02-080470-9

First Collier Books Edition 1974

10   9   8   7   6

Jane's Pocket Book of Major Combat Aircraft is also published in a
hardcover edition by Macmillan Publishing Co., Inc.

Printed in the United States of America

FOREWORD

There have been countless occasions during the 64-year lifetime of JANE'S ALL THE WORLD'S AIRCRAFT when the quick, precise identification of an aeroplane has saved lives. During the Second World War this skill became so vital that the engineering drawings which had been a feature of *Jane's* since the year that Blériot flew the Channel were exchanged for military-type silhouettes in response to official requests. There was usually time to study the shape of an approaching aeroplane before it could fire its guns or drop its bombs, and the eyes and ears of ground observers were as indispensable as radar to locate, track and give warning of intruders.

All that has changed. The aircraft capable of dropping hydrogen bombs in the seventies sometimes fly so high that they cannot be seen clearly, or so low and fast that it is already too late when they come into view. Fighters travelling at twice the speed of sound offer no recognition target for a man with a pair of binoculars. Reconnaissance aircraft at 80 000 ft might as well be satellites so far as an observer is concerned, unless he is seated by a radar screen.

Yet, in an age of electronic countermeasures, decoys, tiny pilotless aeroplanes that give the same radar response as an eight-engined bomber, and a whole range of other instruments of deception, the rapid and precise identification of aircraft is as vital as ever. Not all military aircraft fly at 80 000 ft or Mach 2. Even when they do, fighter pilots must be able to identify them when they attempt an interception. So how can the necessary skill be acquired?

Silhouettes are still used as *ab initio* guides to general shapes, but *Jane's*-style line drawings are at least as good, perhaps better. Best of all is a good photograph, because this is how an aeroplane looks to the viewer. It reveals subtle changes of shape that even the best three-view drawings never suggest, and every detail of equipment and insignia. So the emphasis in this series of aircraft Pocket Books is on the finest available photographs, reproduced as large and as clearly as possible, and backed up by high-quality three-view line drawings.

The information given for each type is that which will best aid its identification, without extraneous facts about its history and structure. Anyone who wants that much detail can find it in the million and a half words of each annual edition of *Jane's*. The Pocket Books are intended as easy-to-handle day-to-day working aids for people whose job or delight it is to recognize aircraft. They are as up-to-date and accurate as *Jane's* itself, being compiled by the same team; their modest cost puts them within reach of anyone who wants a reliable guide to all the world's major types of aircraft. Such a guide and a pair of eyes are all that the recognition expert needs as basic equipment. Proficiency comes from studying every additional photograph on which he can lay hands and every shape in the skies above him.

JOHN W. R. TAYLOR

AERITALIA G91 (Italy)

Single-seat light tactical strike-reconnaissance fighter (G91R and G91Y), and tandem two-seat trainer (G91T)

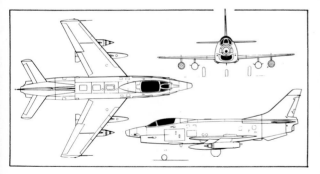

Data: G91Y

Power plant: Two General Electric J85-GE-13A turbojet engines (each 4 080 lb; 1 850 kg st with afterburning)

Wing span: 29 ft 6½ in (9·01 m)

Length overall: 38 ft 3½ in (11·67 m)

Max T-O weight: 19 180 lb (8 700 kg)

Max level speed:
at S/L, 599 knots (690 mph; 1 110 km/h)
at 30 000 ft (9 145 m), Mach 0·95

Max rate of climb:
at S/L, with afterburning: 17 000 ft (5 180 m)/min

Service ceiling: 41 000 ft (12 500 m)

Typical combat radius at S/L: 404 nm (466 miles; 750 km)

Armament: Two 30 mm DEFA cannon in nose; four underwing attachment points for 1 000 lb bombs, 750 lb napalm tanks, 7 × 2 in rocket packs, 28 × 2 in rocket packs or 4 × 5 in rocket containers

Ordered by: Air forces of German Federal Republic (346 G91R/3 and 66 G91T/3), Italy (98 G91R/1/1A/1B, 101 G91T/1 and 55 G91Y*) and Portugal (36 ex-German G91R/4)

*Earlier G91PAN used by Italian Air Force aerobatic team

Photo and Drawing: G91Y

7

AERMACCHI MB 326 (Italy)

Tandem two-seat basic trainer and light attack aircraft

Data: MB 326GB
Power plant: One Rolls-Royce Bristol Viper 20 Mk 540 turbojet engine (3 410 lb; 1 547 kg st)
Wing span: with tip tanks 35 ft 7 in (10·85 m)
Length overall: 34 ft 11¼ in (10·65 m)
Max T-O weight: with fuel in fuselage tank only and 4 325 lb (1 962 kg) armament: 11 500 lb (5 216 kg)
Max level speed: trainer version at typical weight of 8 680 lb (3 937 kg): 468 knots (539 mph; 867 km/h)

Rate of climb at S/L:
   attack version at combat weight of 10 500 lb (4 763 kg): 3 550 ft (1 082 m)/min
Service ceiling:
   attack version at above weight: 39 000 ft (11 900 m)
Combat radius:
   max fuel, 1 695 lb (769 kg) armament, 200 lb (90 kg) fuel reserve, out at 20 000 ft (6 100 m), return at 25 000 ft (7 620 m): 350 nm (403 miles; 648 km)
Armament: Optional; up to 4 000 lb (1 814 kg) of armament can be carried on six underwing attachments. Typical weapon loads include following alternatives: two LAU-3/A packs each containing nineteen 2·75 in FFAR rockets and two packs each containing eight Hispano-Suiza SURA 80 mm rockets; two 12·7 mm gun pods and four packs each containing six SURA 80 mm rockets; one 7·62 mm Minigun, one 12·7 mm gun pod, two Matra 122 rocket packs and two packs each containing six SURA 80 mm rockets; two 500 lb bombs and eight 5 in HVAR rockets; two Nord AS.12 missiles; one 12·7 mm gun pod, one reconnaissance pack containing four Vinten cameras and two 600 lb (272 kg) drop-tanks, or two Matra SA-10 packs each containing a 30 mm Aden gun
Ordered by: Air forces of Argentine (Navy 8 MB 326GB), Australia (97 MB 326H), Brazil (112 MB 326GB, known as AT-26 Xavante), Ghana (5 MB 326F), Italy (100 MB 326), South Africa (100 or more MB 326M, known as Impala), Tunisia (8 MB 326B), Zaïre (17 MB 326GB) and Zambia (18 MB 326GB)

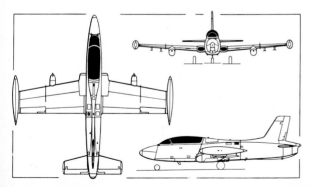

Photo and Drawing: M.B. 326GB   9

AÉROSPATIALE ALOUETTE III (France)

General-purpose, armed reconnaissance and anti-tank helicopter

Data: SA 316B

Power plant: One Turboméca Artouste IIIB turboshaft engine (870 shp, derated to 570 shp)

Main rotor diameter: 36 ft 1¾ in (11·02 m)

Length overall: 42 ft 1½ in (12·84 m), rotors turning

Max T-O weight: 4 850 lb (2 200 kg)

Max level speed at S/L: 113 knots (130 mph; 210 km/h)

Rate of climb at S/L: 885 ft (270 m)/min

Service ceiling: 13 125 ft (4 000 m)

Range with max fuel at S/L: 258 nm (298 miles; 480 km)

Armament:
As assault helicopter: wide range of weapons, including an internally-mounted 7·62 mm AA52 machine-gun or 20 mm MG 151/20 cannon, or four AS.11 or two AS.12 externally-mounted wire-guided missiles. Tests have been successfully completed with HOT missiles.

As naval helicopter: two AS.12 wire-guided missiles. In an ASW role, two Mk 44 homing torpedoes, or one torpedo and MAD gear, can be carried

Ordered by: Air forces of Abu Dhabi (5), Argentine (Navy 4), Austria (10), Bangla Desh (3), Belgium (Coast Guard 3), Burma (13), Denmark (Navy 8), Dominican Republic (1), Ecuador (6), Equatorial Guinea (2), Ethiopia (10), France (Air Force 83, Navy 22, Army 84), Hong Kong (3), India (Air Force 104, Navy 18), Indonesia (Air Force 7, Navy 3, Army), Iraq (12), Irish Republic (Army 4), Israel (approx 15), Ivory Coast (3), Jordan (7), Khmer (8), Laos (4), Lebanon (5), Libya (4), Malagasy (2), Malaysia (29), Mexico (Air Force 6, Navy 4), Morocco (Air Force 4, Army 3), Nepal (1), Netherlands (77), Pakistan (Air Force 4, Navy 4, Army 8), Peru (Air Force 10, Navy 2), Portugal (110), Rhodesia (8), Romania (50 being built for both military and civil use), Saudi Arabia (4), Singapore (8), South Africa (70), Switzerland (83), Tunisia (4), Venezuela (Air Force 5, Army 15), Yugoslavia (20) and Zaïre (8)

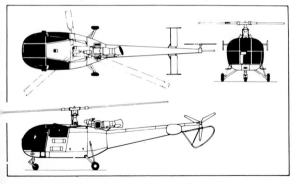

Photo and Drawing: SA 316 Alouette III

11

AEROSPATIALE SUPER FRELON (France)

First flight 1962

Heavy assault and anti-submarine helicopter

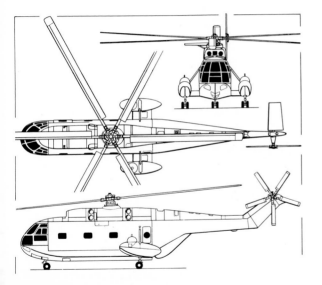

Data: SA 321G Super Frelon
Power plant: Three Turboméca Turmo IIIC6-70 turboshaft engines (each 1 630 shp)
Main rotor diameter: 62 ft 0 in (18·90 m)
Length overall: 75 ft 6⅝ in (23·03 m), rotors turning
Max T-O weight: 28 660 lb (13 000 kg)
Cruising speed at S/L: 135 knots (155 mph; 249 km/h)
Max rate of climb at S/L: 1 312 ft (400 m)/min
Service ceiling: 10 325 ft (3 150 m)
Range at S/L: 442 nm (509 miles; 820 km)
Armament: Four homing torpedoes or two Exocet missiles
Ordered by: Air forces of France (Air Force 1, Navy 24), Iran (16), Israel (12), Libya (9) and South Africa (16)

Photo and Drawing: SA 321G Super Frelon

13

AÉROSPATIALE/WESTLAND PUMA (France/UK)

Assault helicopter

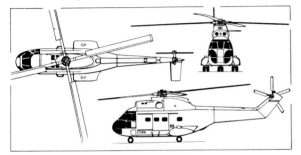

Photo and Drawing: SA 330E Puma HC Mk 1

Data: SA 330E
Power plant: Two Turboméca Turmo IIIC4 turbo-shaft engines (each 1 328 shp)
Main rotor diameter: 49 ft 2½ in (15·00 m)
Length overall: 59 ft 6½ in (18·15 m)
Max T-O weight: 14 770 lb (6 700 kg)
Max cruising speed at S/L: 147 knots (169 mph; 272 km/h)
Max rate of climb at S/L: 1 575 ft (480 m)/min
Service ceiling: 15 100 ft (4 600 m)
Max range at S/L: 334 nm (385 miles; 620 km)
Armament: Wide range of armament can be carried, including side-firing 20 mm cannon, axial-firing 7·62 mm machine-guns, and missiles
Ordered by: Air forces of Abu Dhabi (3), France (Air Force 9, Army 130), Ivory Coast (1), Mexico (3), Portugal (12), South Africa (20 or more), UK (40) and Zaïre (30)

AGUSTA A 106 (Italy)

First flight 1965

Light anti-submarine helicopter

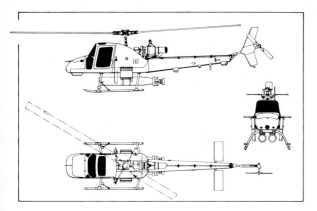

Power plant: One Turboméca-Agusta TAA 230 turboshaft engine (derated to 330 shp for T-O and max continuous rating of 280 shp)

Main rotor diameter: 31 ft 2 in (9·50 m)

Length overall: 36 ft 0 in (10·975 m), rotors turning

Max T-O weight: 3 086 lb (1 400 kg)

Max level speed at S/L: 96 knots (110 mph; 177 km/h)

Max rate of climb at S/L: 1 230 ft (375 m)/min

Hovering ceiling in ground effect: 8 350 ft (2 545 m)

Range at S/L:
max internal fuel: 134 nm (155 miles; 249 km)
max internal and external fuel: 399 nm (460 miles; 740 km)

Armament: Two Mk 44 homing torpedoes

Ordered by: Being evaluated by Italian Navy; production to begin in 1973 if successful

BAC 167 STRIKEMASTER and JET PROVOST (UK)

First flights 1967/1954

Side-by-side two-seat light strike aircraft (Strikemaster, and Jet Provost Mks 51, 52 and 55) and training aircraft (Jet Provost Mks 3, 4 and 5)

Data: Strikemaster
Power plant: One Rolls-Royce Bristol Viper Srs 20 F-20 Mk 535 turbojet engine (3 410 lb; 1 547 kg st)
Wing span: 36 ft 11 in (11·25 m) over tip-tanks
Length overall: 33 ft 8$\frac{1}{2}$ in (10·27 m)
Max T-O weight: 11 500 lb (5 215 kg)
Max level speed with 50% fuel, clean:
 at S/L: 391 knots (450 mph; 724 km/h)
 at 20 000 ft (6 100 m): 410 knots (472 mph; 760 km/h)

Rate of climb at S/L (training, internal fuel):
 5 250 ft (1 600 m)/min
Range with 200 lb (91 kg) fuel reserve:
 at 8 355 lb (3 789 kg) AUW (training): 629 nm (725 miles; 1 166 km)
 at 10 500 lb (4 558 kg) AUW (combat): 1 075 nm (1 238 miles; 1 992 km)
 at 11 500 lb (5 012 kg) AUW (max T-O): 1 200 nm (1 382 miles; 2 224 km)
Armament: Eight underwing hard-points for up to 3 000 lb (1 360 kg) of external stores, or up to 2 650 lb (1 200 kg) with full fuel load. Typical underwing loads include 12 × 3 in Mk 6 rockets with 60 lb warhead, 32 Hispano-Suiza Sura type 3 rockets, 96 × 2 in Mk 1 rockets with 3$\frac{1}{4}$ lb warheads, four 500 lb bombs, four 540 lb retarded bombs, two 50 gal napalm tanks and 72 × 2 in rockets. Two 7·62 mm FN machine-guns can be fitted
Ordered by:
 STRIKEMASTER: Air forces of Ecuador (8 Mk 89), Kenya (6 Mk 87), Kuwait (12 Mk 83), Muscat (8 Mk 82A), New Zealand (10 Mk 88), Oman (12 Mk 82), Saudi Arabia (approx 35 Mk 80), Singapore (16 Mk 84) and South Yemen (4 Mk 81)
 JET PROVOST: Air forces of Iraq (20 T Mk 52), Kuwait (6 T Mk 51), South Yemen (8 T Mk 52), Sri Lanka (12 T Mk 51), Sudan (4 T Mk 51, 4 T Mk 52 and 5 Mk 55), UK (210 T Mk 3, 198 T Mk 4 and 110 T Mk 5) and Venezuela (15 T Mk 52)

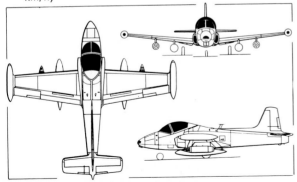

Photo: BAC 167 Strikemaster Mk 84
Drawing: BAC 167 Strikemaster

19

BAC LIGHTNING (UK)

Single-seat supersonic fighter (Mks 2A, 3, 6, 52 and 53) and two-seat operational trainer (Mks 4, 5, 54 and 55)

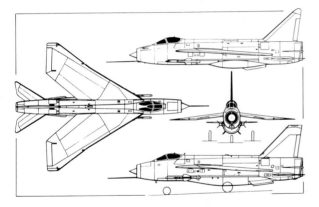

Photo and Drawing: Lightning F Mk 6

Data: Lightning F Mk 53
Power plant: Two Rolls-Royce Avon 302-C turbojet engines (each 16 300 lb; 7 393 kg st with after-burning)
Wing span: 34 ft 10 in (10·61 m)
Length overall: 55 ft 3 in (16·84 m), including probe
Max T-O weight: approx 48 000 lb (21 770 kg)
Max level speed at operational height: above 1 146 knots (1 320 mph; 2 124 km/h)
Armament: Two 30 mm Aden guns can be carried. Weapon bay can accommodate one of a variety of operational packs. These include a twin-Firestreak or twin-Red Top air-to-air missile pack, or a rocket pack with two retractable launchers for a total of 44 × 2 in spin-stabilized rockets. Two pylons beneath outer wings, each capable of carrying two 1 000 lb HE, retarded or fire bombs, two Matra 155 launchers for 18 SNEB 68 mm rockets apiece, two flare pods or two machine-gun pods
Ordered by: Air forces of Kuwait (12 F Mk 53 and 2 T Mk 55), Saudi Arabia (5 F Mk 52, 34 F Mk 53, 2 T Mk 54 and 6 T Mk 55), and UK (30 F Mk 2A, 58 F Mk 3, 20 T Mk 4, 22 T Mk 5 and 67 F Mk 6)

BELL AH-1 HUEYCOBRA and SEACOBRA (USA)

First flight 1965

Single-engined (AH-1G) or twin-engined (AH-1J) armed helicopter

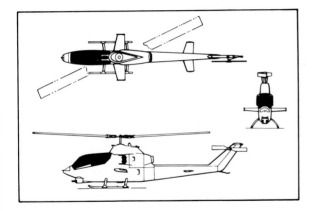

Photo: AH-1J HueyCobra
Drawing: AH-1G HueyCobra

Data: AH-1G HueyCobra
Power plant: One 1 400 shp Lycoming T53-L-13 turboshaft engine (derated to 1 100 shp)
Main rotor diameter: 44 ft 0 in (13·41 m)
Length overall: 52 ft 11½ in (16·14 m), main rotor fore and aft
Max T-O weight: 9 500 lb (4 309 kg)
Max level speed: 190 knots (219 mph; 352 km/h)
Max rate of climb at S/L: 1 230 ft (375 m)/min
Service ceiling: 11 400 ft (3 475 m)
Max range at S/L:
 max fuel, 8% reserves: 310 nm (357 miles; 574 km)
Armament: Two Miniguns, two XM-129 40 mm grenade launchers or one Minigun and one XM-129. Structural provision for an M-61A1 20 mm Vulcan gun, an XM-197 three-barrel 20 mm gun or a three-barrel 30 mm gun. Four external attachment points under stub-wings can accommodate various stores including a total of 76 × 2·75 in rockets in four XM-159 packs, 28 similar rockets in four XM-157 packs, two XM-18E1 Minigun pods or an XM-35 20 mm gun kit. 8 TOW missiles can be fitted on the two inboard stations
Ordered by: Spain (Navy 4 AH-1G), US (Air Force 1 040 AH-1G HueyCobra, Marine Corps 38 AH-1G HueyCobra and 49 AH-1J SeaCobra with a Pratt and Whitney (UACL) T400-CP-400 coupled turboshaft developing 1 250 shp for T-O and 1 100 shp max continuous power), and Iran (202 AH-1J HueyCobra)

Power plant: One Lycoming T53-L-13 turboshaft
    engine (1 400 shp)
Main rotor diameter: 48 ft 0 in (14·63 m)
Length overall: 57 ft 1 in (17·40 m,) blades turning

Max T-O weight: 9 500 lb (4 309 kg)
Max level speed: 110 knots (127 mph; 204 km/h)
Rate of climb at S/L: 1 600 ft (488 m)/min
Service ceiling: 12 600 ft (3 840 m)

BELL UH-1 IROQUOIS and MODELS 204B/205 (USA)

First flights 1956/1963/1961

Utility and search and rescue helicopter

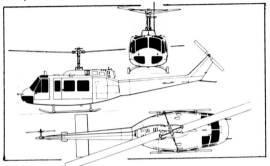

Photo: Agusta-Bell 204AS
Drawing and Data: Model 205 (UH-1H) Iroquois

Range with max fuel:
   no allowances, no reserves, at S/L at max T-O weight:
   276 nm (318 miles; 511 km)
Accommodation: Cabin space of 220 cu ft (6·23 m³) provides room for pilot and 11-14 troops, or six litters and a medical attendant, or 3 880 lb (1 759 kg) of freight
Ordered by: Air forces of Argentine (Air Force 8 UH-1H, Army 7 UH-1H), Australia (Air Force 24 UH-1B, 58 UH-1D and 41 UH-1H, Navy 9 UH-1D), Austria (23 Agusta-Bell 204B), Brazil (6 SH-1D, 12 UH-1D), Brunei (2 Bell 205A), Canada (10 CUH-1H, 50 CUH-1N), Chile (2 UH-1D), Colombia (6 UH-1B), Ethiopia (Air Force 5 Agusta-Bell 204B, Army 6 UH-1H), German Federal Republic (Air Force/Army 352 Dornier-Bell UH-1D), Greece (6 Agusta-Bell 205), Guatemala (6 UH-1), Indonesia (2 Bell 204B), Iran (Navy 4 Agusta-Bell 205A, Army 47 Agusta-Bell 205A), Israel (25 Agusta-Bell 205A), Italy (more than 160 Agusta-Bell 204B/205A), Japan (Army 90 Fuji-Bell UH-1B and 81 Fuji-Bell UH-1H), Khmer (5 UH-1), South Korea (5 UH-1D), Kuwait (6 Agusta-Bell 204B), Laos (UH-1), Morocco (24 Agusta-Bell 205), Netherlands (Navy 7 Agusta-Bell 204B), New Zealand (5 UH-1D, 13 UH-1H), Norway (32 UH-1B), Oman (8 Agusta-Bell 205), Panama (2 UH-1H), Peru (12 UH-1D, 13 UH-1H), Philippines (12 UH-1D), Saudi Arabia (23 Agusta-Bell 204B and 1 Agusta-Bell 205), Spain (Navy 12 Agusta-Bell 204B, Army 12 UH-1B and 16 UH-1H), Sweden (Air Force 6 Agusta-Bell 204B, Army 12 Agusta-Bell 204B), Taiwan (Air Force 24 UH-1H, Army 50 UH-1H), Thailand (50 UH-1H), Turkey (Air Force 10 UH-1D, Navy 3 Agusta-Bell 205A, Army 20 Agusta-Bell 204B), USA (Air Force 146 UH-1F/UH-1P/TH-1F, 30 UH-1H and 79 UH-1N; Navy 27 HH-1K, 45 TH-1L, 8 UH-1L and 24 UH-1N; Marine Corps 148 UH-1E and 67 UH-1N; Army approx 7 000 UH-1A/B/C/D/H/M/N), South Vietnam (approx 625 UH-1) and Zambia (5 Agusta-Bell 205A)

BERIEV M-12 (Be-12) (USSR)

First flight about 1960

NATO Code Name *Mail*
Maritime reconnaissance amphibian

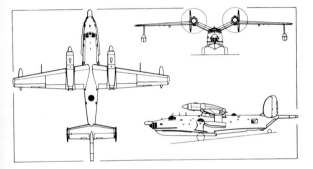

Power plant: Two Ivchenko AI-20D turboprop engines (each 4 000 shp)
Wing span: approx 97 ft 6 in (29·70 m)
Length overall: approx 99 ft 0 in (30·20 m)
Max T-O weight: approx 65 035 lb (29 500 kg)
Max level speed: approx 329 knots (379 mph; 610 km/h)
Max range: approx 2 158 nm (2 485 miles; 4 000 km)
Armament: Internal bomb-bay. Provision for one large and one small external stores pylon under each outer wing panel
Ordered by: Soviet Navy

BOEING B-52 STRATOFORTRESS (USA)

Long-range strategic heavy bomber

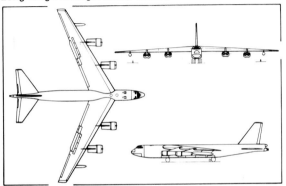

Photo: B-52G Stratofortress
Drawing: B-52H Stratofortress

Data: B-52H Stratofortress
Power plant: Eight Pratt and Whitney TF33-P-3 turbofan engines (each 17 000 lb; 7 718 kg st)
Wing span: 185 ft 0 in (56·39 m)
Length overall: 157 ft 7 in (48·03 m)
Max T-O weight: 488 000 lb (221 350 kg)
Max speed: over 565 knots (650 mph; 1 040 km/h)
Service ceiling: over 60 000 ft (18 300 m)
Max range: 10 855 nm (12 500 miles; 20 120 km)
Armament: One M-61 20 mm gun in General Electric rear turret. Normal offensive load comprises two AGM-28 Hound Dog missiles under wings and bombs in internal weapon-bay. Provision for carrying ADM-20 Quail diversionary missiles internally and/or ALE-25 diversionary rocket pods under wings. Ninety-six B-52G/H each being modified to carry eight SRAM (Short Range Attack Missiles) in weapon-bay and six under each wing
Ordered by: US Air Force (170 B-52D, 100 B-52E, 89 B-52F, 193 B-52G and 102 B-52H; from these, approx 450 remain in service)

BOEING E-3A (USA)

Airborne warning and control system (AWACS) aircraft

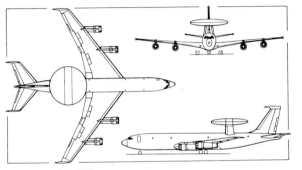

Power plant: Four Pratt and Whitney TF33-P-7A turbofan engines (each 21 000 lb; 9 525 kg st)
Wing span: 145 ft 9 in (44·42 m)
Length overall: 152 ft 11 in (46·61 m)
Accommodation: Operational crew of 17, which may be increased according to mission
Ordered by: Under development for US Air Force. First of 2 EC-137D prototypes (converted from Boeing 707-320) flown 9 February 1972; planned procurement, subject to satisfactory development progress, of 5 pre-production and 42 E-3A production aircraft

Photo: EC-137D prototype
Drawing: E-3A

BOEING KC-97 STRATOFREIGHTER (USA)

Transport and flight refuelling tanker

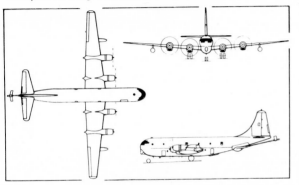

Photo: KC-97L
Drawing: KC-97G

Data: KC-97G
Power plant: Four Pratt and Whitney R-4360-59B piston-engines (each 3 500 hp); KC-97L has two underwing auxiliary J47-GE-25A jet engines
Wing span: 141 ft 3 in (43·05 m)
Length overall: 117 ft 5 in (35·78 m), including refuelling boom
Max T-O weight: 175 000 lb (79 450 kg)
Max speed: 325 knots (375 mph; 603 km/h)
Max range: 3 735 nm (4 300 miles; 6 920 km)
Ordered by: Air forces of Israel (approx 12) Spain (3) and USA (888)

BOEING KC-135 STRATOTANKER, EC-135 and RC-135 (USA)

First flight 1956

Flight refuelling tanker (KC-135), airborne relay communications (EC-135) or electronics reconnaissance (RC-135) aircraft

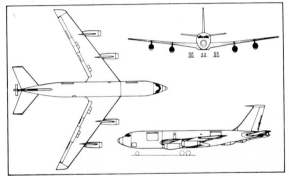

Photo: RC-135M
Drawing: KC-135A Stratotanker

Data: KC-135A Stratotanker
Power plant: Four Pratt and Whitney J57-P-59W turbojet engines (each 13 750 lb; 6 237 kg st)
Wing span: 130 ft 10 in (39·88 m)
Length overall: 136 ft 3 in (41·53 m)
Max T-O weight: 297 000 lb (134 715 kg)
Average cruising speed:
    at 30 500-45 000 ft (9 300-13 700 m): 462 knots (532 mph; 856 km/h)
Rate of climb at S/L: 1 290 ft (393 m)/min
Service ceiling: 50 000 ft (15 240 m)
Transfer radius:
    with 6 734 lb (3 055 kg) fuel reserve: 1 000 nm (1 150 miles; 1 850 km)
Ordered by: Air forces of France (12 C-135F), Iran (5) and USA (Air Force, 732 KC-135A/Q/R/T, of which some converted to EC-135A/G/H/K/L/P; 17 EC-135C/J; and 4 RC-135A and 10 RC-135B, of which some converted to RC-135D/MS)

BOEING VERTOL/KAWASAKI MODEL 107/H-46 SEA KNIGHT SERIES (USA/Japan)

First flight 1958

Transport, anti-submarine and general utility helicopter

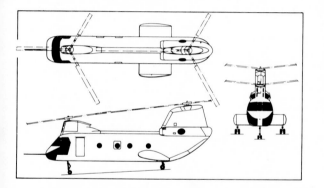

Photo: CH-46A Sea Knight
Drawing: CH-46D Sea Knight

Data: CH-46F Sea Knight
Power plant: Two General Electric T58-GE-10 turboshaft engines (each 1 400 shp)
Rotor diameter: (each) 51 ft 0 in (15·54 m)
Length overall: 84 ft 4 in (25·70 m), blades turning
Max T-O weight: 23 000 lb (10 433 kg)
Max permissible speed:
at AUW of 20 800 lb (9 435 kg): 144 knots (166 mph; 267 km/h)
Max rate of climb at S/L: 1 715 ft (523 m)/min
Service ceiling: 14 000 ft (4 265 m)
Range at AUW of 20 800 lb;(9 435 kg):
with 4 275 lb (1 939 kg) payload, 10% fuel reserve: 206 nm (237 miles; 381 km)
Accommodation: Crew of 3, twenty-five troops and troop commander. Alternatively, up to 4 000 lb (1 814 kg) of cargo can be carried,
Ordered by: Air forces of Canada (6 CH-113 Labrador and 12 CH-113A Voyageur), Japan (Air SDF 30, Ground SDF 76, Maritime SDF 16 Kawasaki KV-107/II), Sweden (Air Force 10 HKP 4, Navy 3 HKP 4 and 7 HKP 7), Thailand (4 Kawasaki KV-107/II) and USA (Navy/Marine Corps, more than 500 CH-46A/D, UH-46A/D, CH-46E/F and RH-46A)

BOEING VERTOL CH-47 CHINOOK (USA)

First flight 1961

Medium transport helicopter

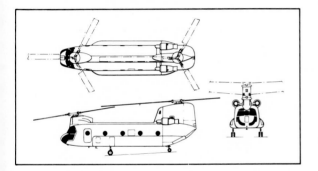

Photo and Drawing: CH-47A Chinook

Data: CH-47C Chinook
Power plant: Two Lycoming T55-L-11 turboshaft engines (each 3 750 shp)
Rotor diameter: (each) 60 ft 0 in (18·29 m)
Length overall: 99 ft 0 in (30·18 m), rotors turning
Take-off weight: 46 000 lb (20 865 kg)
Max speed at S/L: 123 knots (142 mph; 229 km/h), with max payload
Max rate of climb at S/L: 1 320 ft (402 m)/min, with max payload
Service ceiling: 8 000 ft (2 440 m), with max payload
Max ferry range:
   integral and internal auxiliary fuel only; cruise at optimum altitude and standard temperature; no payload; 10% fuel reserve: 1 233 nm (1 420 miles; 2 285 km)
Accommodation: Crew of 2 or 3; 33 to 44 troops, or 24 litters and two attendants, or 23 450 lb (10 637 kg) of freight can be carried in main cabin
Ordered by: Air forces of Australia (12 CH-47C), Iran (Air Force 2 CH-47C, Army 16 CH-47C), Italy (Army 26 CH-47C), Spain (Army 6 CH-47C), USA (Army approx 700 CH-47A/B/C) and South Vietnam (approx 50)

BREGUET ALIZÉ (France)

Carrier-borne anti-submarine aircraft

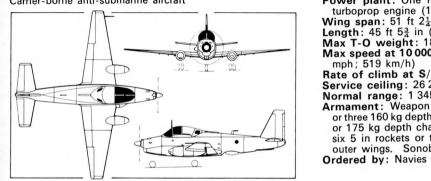

Power plant: One Rolls-Royce Dart RDa 7 Mk 21 turboprop engine (1 975 shp)
Wing span: 51 ft $2\frac{1}{4}$ in (15·60 m)
Length: 45 ft $5\frac{3}{4}$ in (13·86 m)
Max T-O weight: 18 078 lb (8 200 kg)
Max speed at 10 000 ft (3 050 m): 280 knots (322 mph; 519 km/h)
Rate of climb at S/L: 1 380 ft (420 m)/min
Service ceiling: 26 250 ft (8 000 m)
Normal range: 1 345 nm (1 550 miles; 2 500 km)
Armament: Weapon-bay accommodates a torpedo or three 160 kg depth charges. Racks for two 160 kg or 175 kg depth charges under inner wings and for six 5 in rockets or two Nord SS.11 missiles under outer wings. Sonobuoys in front of wheel fairings
Ordered by: Navies of France (75) and India (12)

BREGUET ATLANTIC (France)

Long-range maritime patrol aircraft

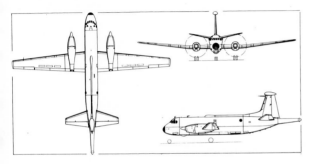

Power plant: Two SNECMA-built Rolls-Royce Tyne RTy 20 Mk 21 turboprop engines (each 6 105 ehp)
Wing span: 119 ft 1 in (36·30 m)
Length overall: 104 ft 2 in (31·75m)
Max T-O weight: 95 900 lb (43 500 kg)
Max level speed:
   at high altitudes: 355 knots (409 mph; 658 km/h)
Service ceiling: 32 800 ft (10 000 m)
Max range: 4 854 nm (5 590 miles; 9 000 km)
Armament: Main weapons carried in fuselage bay. Weapons include all NATO standard bombs, 175 kg French or 385 lb US depth charges, HVAR rockets, homing torpedoes, including types such as the Mk 44 Brush or LX 4 with acoustic heads, or four underwing air-to-surface missiles with nuclear or HE warheads
Ordered by: Navies of France (40), Federal Germany (20), Italy (18) and the Netherlands (9)

CANADAIR CL-41/CT-114 TUTOR (Canada)

First flight 1960

Side-by-side two-seat light attack aircraft (CL-41G) and jet basic trainer (CT-114)

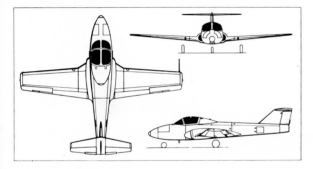

Photo: CL-41G Tebuan
Drawing: CT-114 Tutor

Data: CL-41G
Power plant: One General Electric J85-J4 turbojet engine (2 950 lb; 1 340 kg st)
Wing span: 36 ft 5·9 in (11·13 m)
Length overall: 32 ft 0 in (9·75 m)
Max T-O weight: 11 288 lb (5 131 kg)
Max level speed:
at 28 500 ft (8 700 m) with 50% fuel and no external stores: 417 knots (480 mph; 774 km/h)
Service ceiling: 42 200 ft (12 800 m)
Armament: Up to 3 500 lb (1 590 kg) of gun pods, bombs, rockets and air-to-air missiles can be carried with max internal fuel
Ordered by: Air forces of Canada (190 CT-114 Tutor) and Malaysia (20 CL-41G Tebuan)

CANADAIR CP-107 ARGUS (Canada)

First flight 1957

Long-range maritime patrol aircraft

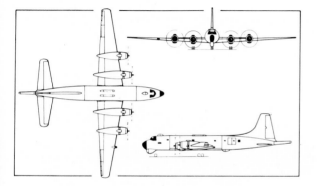

Photo and Drawing: CP-107 Argus Mk 2

Data: CP-107 Argus Mk 2
Power plant: Four Wright R-3350 (TC18EA1) turbo compound engines (each 3 700 hp)
Wing span: 142 ft 3½ in (43·37 m)
Length overall: 128 ft 3 in (39·09 m)
T-O weight: 148 000 lb (67 130 kg)
Max speed: 273 knots (315 mph; 507 km/h)
Service ceiling: over 20 000 ft (6 100 m)
Range: over 3 475 nm (4 000 miles; 6 440 km)
Armament: Two bomb-bays each can accommodate 4 000 lb (1 815 kg) of stores, including homing torpedoes. Provision for carrying two 3 800 lb (1 724 kg) missiles under outer wings
Ordered by: Canadian Armed Forces (13 Mk 1 and 20 Mk 2)

CESSNA A-37 and T-37 (USA)

Light attack aircraft (A-37) and basic jet trainer (T-37)

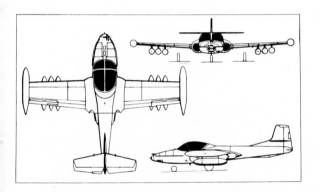

Photo: A-37B
Drawing: A-37A
Data: A-37B
Power plant: Two General Electric J85-GE-17A turbojet engines (each 2 850 lb; 1 293 kg st)
Wing span: 35 ft 10½ in (10·93 m) over tip-tanks
Length overall: 29 ft 3½ in (8·93 m)
Max T-O weight: 14 000 lb (6 350 kg)

Max level speed:
at 16 000 ft (4 875 m): 440 knots (507 mph; 816 km/h)
Rate of climb at S/L: 6 990 ft (2 130 m)/min
Service ceiling: 41 765 ft (12 730 m)
Range with max payload:
including 4 100 lb (1 860 kg) ordnance: 399 nm (460 miles; 740 km)
Armament: GAU-2B/A 7·62 mm Minigun installed in forward fuselage. Each wing has four pylon stations, the two inner ones carrying 870 lb (394 kg) each, the intermediate one 600 lb (272 kg) and the outer one 500 lb (227 kg). The following weapons, in various combinations, can be carried on the underwing pylons. SUU-20 bomb and rocket pod, MK-81 or MK-82 bomb, BLU/32/B fire bomb, SUU-11/A gun pod, CBU-24/B or CBU-25/A dispenser and bomb, M-117 demolition bomb, LAU-3/A rocket pod, CBU-12/A, CBU-14/A, or CBU-22/A dispenser and bomb, BLU-1C/B fire bomb, LAU-32/A or LAU-59/A rocket pod, CBU-19/A canister cluster and SUU-25/A flare launcher
Ordered by: Air forces of Brazil (65 T-37C), Chile (10 T-37B), Colombia (10 T-37C), Federal Germany (47 T-37B, based in the US), Greece (20 T-37C), Khmer (6 T-37B), Pakistan (12 T-37B and 12 T-37C), Peru (26 T-37B/C), Portugal (30 T-37C), Thailand (8 T-37B), Turkey (23 T-37C), USA (Air Force, over 900 T-37A/B and 329 A-37B) and South Vietnam (194 A-37A/B, ex-USAF)

weather single-seat interceptor fighter (F-102A)
two-seat combat trainer (TF-102A)

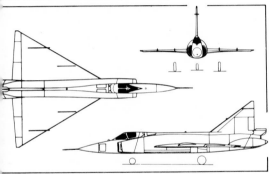

to and Drawing: F-102A Delta Dagger

Data: F-102A Delta Dagger
Power plant: One Pratt and Whitney J57-P-23 or -25 turbojet engine (17 200 lb; 7 800 kg st with after-burning)
Wing span: 38 ft 1½ in (11·62 m)
Length: 68 ft 4½ in (20·84 m)
Max T-O weight: 32 000 lb (14 515 kg)
Max speed at 36 000 ft (11 000 m): 716 knots (825 mph; 1 327 km/h)
Service ceiling: 54 000 ft (16 460 m)
Range: approx 955 nm (1 100 miles; 1 770 km)
Armament: Internal missile bay normally carries one Hughes AIM-26A and three AIM-4C Falcons.
Ordered by: Air forces of Turkey (25) and USA (Air Force 975 F-102A and 63 TF-102A)

CONVAIR F-106 DELTA DART (USA)

First flight 1956

Single-seat interceptor fighter (F-106) and two-seat combat trainer (F-106B)

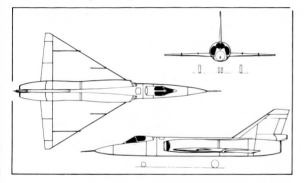

Photo and Drawing: F-106A Delta Dart

Data: F-106A Delta Dart
Power plant: One Pratt and Whitney J75-P-17 turbojet engine (24 500 lb; 11 113 kg st with afterburning)
Wing span: 38 ft 3½ in (11·67 m)
Length overall: 70 ft 8¾ in (21·56 m)
Max T-O weight: over 35 000 lb (15 875 kg)
Max level speed at 36 000 ft (11 000 m): 1 324 knots (1 525 mph; 2 455 km/h)
Service ceiling: 57 000 ft (17 375 m)
Range with max fuel: approx 1 300 nm (1 500 miles; 2 400 km)
Armament: One AIR-2A Genie or AIR-2B Super Genie rocket, four Hughes AIM-4F or AIM-4G Super Falcon air-to-air missiles in internal weapon bay
Ordered by: US Air Force (257 F-106A and 63 F-106B)

DASSAULT ÉTENDARD IV (France)

First flight 1958

Single-seat carrier-based strike fighter/tanker (IV-M)
and tactical reconnaissance aircraft/tanker (IV-P)

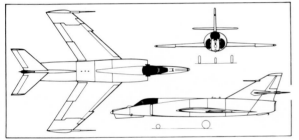

Photo: Etendard IV-P
Drawing: Étendard IV-M

Data: Étendard IV-M
Power plant: One SNECMA Atar 08B turbojet engine
(9 700 lb; 4 400 kg st)
Wing span: 31 ft 6 in (9·60 m)
Length overall: 47 ft 3 in (14·40 m)
Max T-O weight: 22 650 lb (10 275 kg)
Max level speed:
at 36 000 ft (11 000 m): 585 knots (674 mph;
1 085 km/h)
Rate of climb at S/L: 19 700 ft (6 000 m)/min
Service ceiling: 49 200 ft (15 000 m)
Combat range:
low-level attack role: 321 nm (370 miles; 600 km)
medium-altitude mission: 868 nm (1 000 miles;
1 600 km)
Armament: Two 30 mm DEFA cannon. Four under-
wing attachments for up to 3 000 lb (1 360 kg) of
rockets, bombs, Nord 5103 air-to-surface or Sidewinder air-to-air missiles or external fuel tanks
Ordered by: French Navy (69 Étendard IV-M,
including 19 equipped as 'buddy' tankers, and 21
Étendard IV-P tactical reconnaissance/tankers);
Super Étendard under development for French Navy

DASSAULT MIRAGE III (France)
(III C/E/O/S)

Single-seat fighter-bomber and tactical reconnaissance aircraft (III-R); two-seat combat trainer (III-B/D)

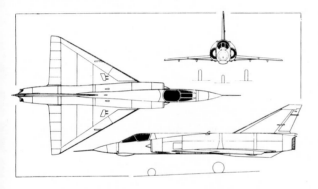

Photo: Mirage III-EP
Drawing: Mirage III-E
Data: Mirage III-E
Power plant: One SNECMA Atar 09C turbojet engine (13 670 lb; 6 200 kg st with afterburning); optional and jettisonable SEPR 844 rocket motor (3 300 lb; 1 500 kg st)

Wing span: 27 ft 0 in (8·22 m)
Length overall: 49 ft 3½ in (15·03 m)
Max T-O weight: 29 760 lb (13 500 kg)
Max level speed at 39 375 ft (12 000 m): 1 268 knots (1 460 mph; 2 350 km/h)
Time to 36 000 ft (11 000 m), Mach 0·9: 3 min
Service ceiling at Mach 1·8: 55 775 ft (17 000 m)
Ceiling, using rocket motor: 75 450 ft (23 000 m)
Combat radius, ground attack: 647 nm (745 miles; 1 200 km)
Armament: Ground attack armament consists normally of two 30 mm DEFA cannon in fuselage and two 1 000 lb bombs, or an AS 30 air-to-surface missile under fuselage and 1 000 lb bombs under the wings. Alternative under-wing stores include JL-100 pods, each with 18 rockets, and 55 Imp gallon (250 litre) fuel tanks. For interception duties, one Matra R 530 air-to-air missile can be carried under fuselage, with optional guns and two Sidewinder missiles
Ordered by: Air forces of Argentine (2 III-D and 10 III-E), Australia (16 III-D, 2 III-E, 50 III-OA and 48 III-OF), Brazil (4 III-D and 12 III-E), France (40 III-B/BE, 150 III-C, 180 III-E, 50 III-R and 20 III-RD), Israel (3 III-B and 72 III-C), Lebanon (2 III-B and 10 III-E), Pakistan (3 III-D, 18 III-E and 3 III-R), South Africa (3 III-B, 16 III-C, 3 III-D, 16 III-E and 4 III-R), Spain (4 III-D and 26 III-E), Switzerland (3 III-B, 1 III-C, 18 III-R and 36 III-S) and Venezuela (2 III-D and 13 III-E)

DASSAULT MIRAGE IV-A (France)

First flight 1959

Two-seat supersonic strategic bomber

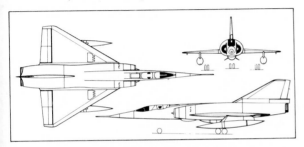

Power plant: Two SNECMA Atar 09K-50 turbojet engines (each 15 430 lb; 7 000 kg st with afterburning)
Wing span: 38 ft 10½ in (11·85 m)
Length overall: 77 ft 1¼ in (23·50 m)
Average T-O weight: 69 665 lb (31 600 kg)
Max speed at 36 000 ft (11 000 m): 1 262 knots (1 454 mph; 2 340 km/h)
Service ceiling: 65 600 ft (20 000 m)
Tactical radius: 668 nm (770 miles; 1 240 km)
Armament: One nuclear weapon semi-recessed under fuselage or 16 × 1 000 lb bombs or four Martel air-to-surface missiles under wings and fuselage
Ordered by: French Air Force (62)

DASSAULT MIRAGE 5 (France)

Single-seat fighter-bomber and reconnaissance aircraft;
two-seat combat trainer

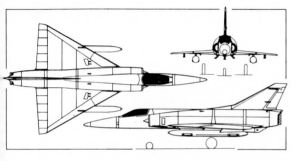

Photo: Mirage 5- P
Power plant: One SNECMA Atar 09C turbojet engine
  (13 670 lb; 6 200 kg st with afterburning)
Wing span: 27 ft 0 in (8·22 m)
Length overall: 51 ft 0¼ in (15·55 m)

Max T-O weight: 29 760 lb (13 500 kg)
Max level speed at 39 375 ft (12 000 m): 1 268
  knots (1 460 mph; 2 350 km/h)
Time to 36 000 ft (11 000 m), Mach 0·9: 3 min
Service ceiling at Mach 1·8: 55 775 ft (17 000 m)
Combat radius with 2 000 lb (907 kg) bomb load:
  high-low-high: 699 nm (805 miles; 1 300 km)
  low-low-low: 347 nm (400 miles; 650 km)
Armament: Ground attack armament consists normally
  of two 30 mm DEFA cannon in fuselage, and two
  1 000 lb bombs or an AS 30 air-to-surface missile
  under fuselage and 1 000 lb bombs under wings.
  Alternative underwing stores include JL-100 pods,
  each with 18 × 68 mm rockets and 55 Imp gallons
  (250 litres) of fuel. For interception duties, one
  Matra R 530 air-to-air missile can be carried under
  the fuselage, with optional guns and two Sidewinder
  missiles
Ordered by: Air forces of Belgium (63 5-BA, 27 5-BR
  and 16 5-BD), Brazil (13 single-seat and 3 two-seat),
  Colombia (10 5-COA, 3 5-COD and 5 5-COR),
  France (50 5-F), Libya (50 5-D/DD/DE/DR),
  Pakistan (28 single-seat and 2 two-seat), Peru (14
  5-P and 2 5-DP) and Venezuela (13 5-V and 2
  5-DV)

DASSAULT MIRAGE F1 (France)

First flight 1966

Single-seat all-weather multi-purpose fighter

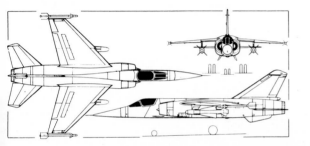

Data: Initial production version (F1-C)
Power plant: One SNECMA Atar 09K-50 turbojet
engine (15 798 lb; 7 166 kg st with afterburning)
Wing span: 27 ft 6¾ in (8·40 m)

Length overall: 49 ft 2½ in (15·00 m)
Max T-O weight: 32 850 lb (14 900 kg)
Max level speed:
high altitude: 1 259 knots (1 450 mph; 2 334 km/h)
low altitude: 794 knots (915 mph; 1 472 km/h)
Max rate of climb at high altitude:
with afterburning: 47 835 ft (14 580 m)/min
Service ceiling: 65 600 ft (20 000 m)
Endurance: 3 hr 45 min
Armament: Two 30 mm DEFA 553 cannon in lower
front fuselage. Two Alkan universal stores attachment pylons under each wing and one under centre
fuselage, plus provision for carrying one air-to-air
missile at each wingtip. Max external combat load
8 820 lb (4 000 kg). Externally-mounted weapons
for interception role include Matra R 530 or Super 530
radar homing or infra-red homing air-to-air missiles
on under-fuselage and inboard wing pylons, and/or
a Sidewinder or Matra 550 Magic infra-red homing
air-to-air missile at each wingtip station. For ground
attack duties, typical loads may include one AS 37
Martel anti-radar missile or AS 30 air-to-surface
missile, eight 450 kg bombs, four launchers each
containing 18 air-to-ground rockets, or six 132 Imp
gallon (600 litre) napalm tanks
Ordered by: Air forces of France (85) Spain (15) and
South Africa

DASSAULT MYSTÈRE IV-A (France)

Single-seat fighter-bomber

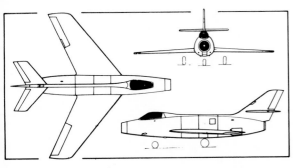

Power plant: One Hispano-Suiza Verdon 350 turbojet engine (7 716 lb; 3 500 kg st)
Wing span: 36 ft 5½ in (11·12 m)
Length overall: 42 ft 1½ in (12·85 m)
Max T-O weight: 18 700 lb (8 480 kg)
Max level speed at S/L: 603 knots (695 mph; 1 118 km/h)
Rate of climb at S/L: 8 850 ft (2 700 m)/min
Endurance: 1 hr 10 min on internal fuel
Armament: Two 30 mm cannon and a pack of rockets in fuselage.   Underwing racks for two 1 000 lb bombs, or napalm tanks, packs of either 6 air-to-ground rockets or 19 air-to-air rockets
Ordered by: Air forces of France (251), India (110) and Israel (60)

DASSAULT SUPER MYSTERE B-2 (France)

Single-seat interceptor and tactical strike fighter

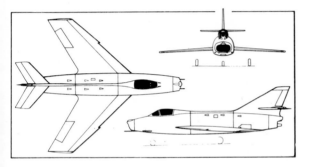

Power plant: One SNECMA Atar 101 G turbojet engine (9 700 lb; 4 400 kg st with afterburning)
Wing span: 34 ft 5¾ in (10·51 m)
Length overall: 46 ft 1 in (14·04 m)
Max T-O weight: 22 046 lb (10 000 kg)
Max level speed at 36 000 ft (11 000 m): 645 knots (743 mph; 1 195 km/h)
Rate of climb:
at 19 840 lb (9 000 kg) AUW: 17 500 ft (5 340 m)/min
Service ceiling: 55 775 ft (17 000 m)
Range: 520 nm (600 miles; 965 km)
Armament: Two 30 mm DEFA cannon and a pack of air-to-air rockets in fuselage. Underwing loads are made up of 38 rockets in two packs, or two 500 kg bombs, two napalm tanks, 12 air-to-surface rockets or two Matra air-to-air guided missiles
Ordered by: Air forces of France (156) and Israel (24)

DE HAVILLAND VAMPIRE (UK)

Single-seat fighter-bomber and side-by-side two-seat trainer

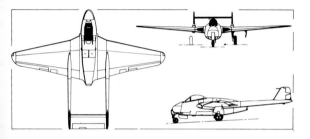

Photo: Vampire T Mk 55
Drawing: Vampire F Mk 1

Data: Vampire FB Mk 6
Power plant: One de Havilland Goblin 3 turbojet engine (3 350 lb; 1 520 kg st)
Wing span: 38 ft 0 in (11·58 m)
Length overall: 30 ft 9 in (9·37 m)
Max T-O weight: 12 390 lb (5 620 kg)
Max level speed at 30 000 ft (9 150 m): 476 knots (548 mph; 882 km/h)
Max range at 30 000 ft (9 150 m):
at 304 knots (350 mph; 563 km/h): 1 060 nm (1 220 miles; 1 960 km)
Armament: Four 20 mm cannon in nose. Underwing stores of up to 2 000 lb (907 kg) including bombs and rockets
Ordered by: Air forces of Dominican Republic (approx 20 F Mk 1/FB Mk 50), India (Air Force/Navy approx 100 T Mk 55), Irish Republic (6 T Mk 55) and Rhodesia (12 FB Mk 9 and 15 T Mk 55)

DE HAVILLAND VENOM (UK)

Single-seat fighter-bomber

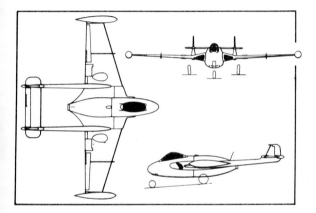

Photo and Drawing: Venom FB Mk 4

Data: Venom FB Mk 50
Power plant: One de Havilland Ghost 103 turbojet engine (4 850 lb; 2 200 kg st)
Wing span: 41 ft 8 in (12·70 m)
Length overall: 31 ft 10 in (9·70 m)
Max T-O weight: 15 400 lb (6 985 kg)
Max level speed: 556 knots (640 mph; 1 030 km/h)
Service ceiling: 49 200 ft (15 545 m)
Range with external tanks: over 868 nm (1 000 miles; 1 610 km)
Armament: Four 20 mm cannon in nose. Underwing stores of up to 2 000 lb (907 kg) including bombs and rockets
Ordered by: Air forces of Switzerland (100 FB Mk 4 and 150 FB Mk 50) and Venezuela (10 FB Mk 4)

DOUGLAS A-1 SKYRAIDER (USA)

First flight 1945

Single- and two-seat counter-insurgency attack bomber and armed escort

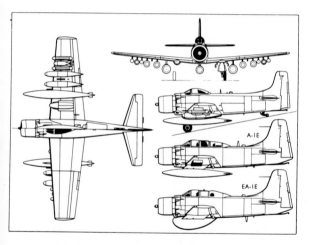

Photo: A-1E Skyraider
Drawing: A-1J Skyraider, with additional side views of A-1E and EA-1E

Data: A-1J Skyraider
Power plant: One Wright R-3350-26WB piston engine (3 050 hp)
Wing span: 50 ft 9 in (15·47 m)
Length overall: 38 ft 10 in (11·84 m)
Max T-O weight: 25 000 lb (11 350 kg)
Max level speed at 18 000 ft (5 485 m): 276 knots (318 mph; 512 km/h)
Max range with external tanks: 2 600 nm (3 000 miles; 4 825 km)
Armament: Four 20 mm cannon in wings. Underwing stores of up to 8 000 lb (3 625 kg)
Ordered by: Air forces of France (100 A-1D), Khmer (approx 14 ex-French A-1D), USA (Air Force/Navy 670 A-1E/EA-1E, 713 A-1H and 72 A-1J), and South Vietnam (more than 50 A-1E/H)

DOUGLAS A-3 SKYWARRIOR (USA)

First flight 1952

Three-seat carrier-borne attack bomber (A-3), reconnaissance bomber (RA-3 and EA-3) and refuelling tanker (KA-3)

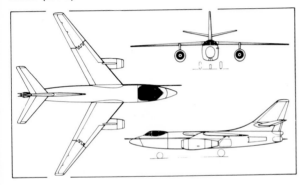

Data: EA-3B Skywarrior
Power plant: Two Pratt & Whitney J57-P-10 turbojet engines (each 10 500 lb; 4 760 kg st)
Wing span: 72 ft 6 in (22·10 m)
Length overall: 76 ft 4 in (23·27 m)
Max T-O weight: 73 000 lb (33 110 kg)
Max level speed at 10 000 ft (3 050 m): 530 knots (610 mph; 982 km/h)
Range: over 2 520 nm (2 900 miles; 4 665 km)
Equipment: specialised ECM equipment
Ordered by: US Navy (50 A-3A/EA-3A/YRA-3A/TA-3A, 164 A-3B, 30 RA-3B, 24 EA-3B and 12 TA-3B/VA-3B; most of those still in service now converted to KA-3B or EKA-3B)

Photo: EKA-3B Skywarrior
Drawing: A-3B Skywarrior

DOUGLAS B-66 DESTROYER (USA)

First flight 1954

Three-seat tactical light bomber (B-66 and RB-66) and electronic (EB-66) or weather reconnaissance (WB-66) aircraft

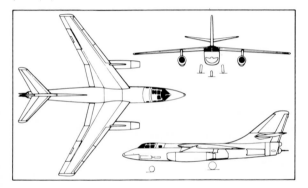

Photo: EB-66C Destroyer
Drawing: B-66B Destroyer

Data: EB-66C Destroyer
Power plant: Two Allison J71-A-13 turbojet engines (each 10 000 lb; 4 535 kg st)
Wing span: 72 ft 6 in (22·10 m)
Length overall: 75 ft 2 in (22·91 m)
Max T-O weight: 83 000 lb (37 648 kg)
Max level speed at 10 000 ft (3 050 m): 538 knots (620 mph; 998 km/h)
Range: 1 300 nm (1 500 miles; 2 410 km)
Equipment: specialized ECM equipment
Ordered by: US Air Force (5 RB-66A and 209 RB-66B/B-66B/RB-66C/WB-66D; most B and C models still in service now converted to EB-66B/C/F)

ENGLISH ELECTRIC CANBERRA (UK)

Three-seat tactical light bomber, interdictor/strike and photographic reconnaissance aircraft

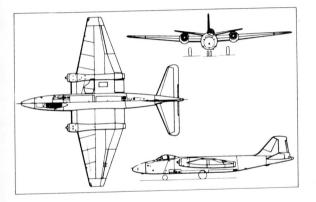

Photo: Canberra B Mk 62
Drawing: Canberra PR Mk 9

Data: Canberra B Mk 6
Power plant: Two Rolls-Royce Avon 109 turbojet engines (each 7 400 lb; 3 355 kg st)
Wing span: 63 ft 11½ in (19·50 m)
Length overall: 65 ft 6 in (19·96 m)
Max T-O weight: 55 000 lb (24 945 kg)
Max level speed at 30 000 ft (9 145 m): 504 knots (580 mph; 930 km/h)
Range: 3 290 nm (3 790 miles; 6 100 km)
Armament: In bomber role can carry 6 000 lb (2 720 kg) of weapons internally. Up to 2 000 lb (907 kg) of external stores including bombs, rocket pods or guided weapons can be carried on underwing pylons on later, modified aircraft
Ordered by: Air forces of Argentine (10 B Mk 62 and 2 T Mk 64), Australia (50 B Mk 20 and 9 T Mk 21), Ecuador (6 B Mk 6), Ethiopia (4 B Mk 52), France (6 B Mk 6), German Federal Republic (4 B Mk 2), India (10 PR Mk 57, 72 B(I) Mk 58, 12 B Mk 66, 12 T Mks 54/67), Peru (12 B Mks 2/72, 2 T Mks 4/74, 8 B(I) Mk 8, 6 B Mk 56 and B(I) Mks 68/78), Rhodesia (15 B Mk 2 and 3 T Mk 4), South Africa (3 T Mk 4 and 6 B(I) Mk 12), Sweden (2 T Mk 11), UK (Air Force approx 70 T Mk 4, B Mk 6, 74 PR Mk 7, B(I) Mk 8, 23 PR Mk 9, B Mk 15 and E Mk 15, T Mk 17, 18 TT Mk 18, and T Mk 19; Navy 6 TT Mk 18 and B Mk 22), and Venezuela (18 B Mks 2/82/B(I) Mk 82, 2 PR Mks 3/83, 2 T Mks 4/84 and 8 B(I) Mks 8/88). *See also* Martin B-57

FAIRCHILD REPUBLIC A-10A (USA)

First flight 1972

Single-seat close-support aircraft

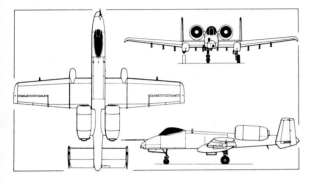

Data: Prototypes
Power plant: Two General Electric TF34 high by-pass ratio turbofan engines (each approx 9 000 lb; 4 080 kg st)

Wing span: 54 ft 8 in (16·66 m)
Length overall: 54 ft 8 in (16·66 m)
Max T-O weight (estimated): 45 825 lb (20 786 kg)
Armament: Multi-barrel forward-firing 30 mm (20 mm on prototypes) gun mounted in the nose. Five pylons under each wing, two inboard and three outboard of main-wheel fairing, to allow carriage of a wide range of stores including 24 × 500 lb Mk-82 LDGP, 24 × 500 lb Mk-82 retarded, 16 × 750 lb M-117 LDGP, 16 × 750 lb M-117 retarded or 4 × 2 000 lb Mk-84 general purpose bombs; 8 BLU-1 or BLU-27/8 incendiary bombs; 4 × SUU-25 or SUU-42 flare launchers; 20 Rockeye 11 cluster bombs, 16 CBU-24/49, 8 CBU-43 or 12 CBU-60 dispenser weapons; 9 AGM-65 Maverick and 2 AIM-9E/J Sidewinder missiles; Mk-82 and Mk-84 laser-guided bombs; Mk-84 EO-guided bombs; 2 SUU-23 or recoilless-gun pods

Ordered by: US Air Force (2 prototypes for evaluation and 10 pre-production models)

FAIRCHILD INDUSTRIES AC-119 GUNSHIP (USA)

First flight 1967

Twin-engined (AC-119G) or four-engined (AC-119K) armed transport for interdiction and ground defence suppression

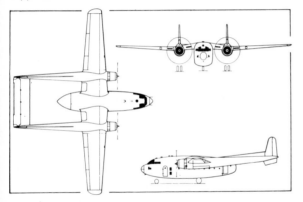

Photo: AC-119K
Drawing: C-119G

Data: AC-119K
Power plant: Two Wright R-3350-89B piston engines (each 3 700 hp) plus two General Electric J85-GE-17 auxiliary jet engines (each 2 850 lb; 1 293 kg st)
Wing span: 109 ft 3 in (33·30 m)
Length overall: 89 ft 5 in (27·25 m)
Max T-O weight: 80 400 lb (36 468 kg)
Max level speed at 10 000 ft (3 050 m): 217 knots (250 mph; 402 km/h)
Max rate of climb at S/L, one engine out: 900 ft (274 m)/min
Service ceiling, one engine out: 23 500 ft (7 163 m)
Range with max payload of 4 838 lb (2 194 kg): 1 720 nm (1 980 miles; 3 186 km)
Armament: Four side-firing 7·62 mm General Electric Miniguns and two 20 mm cannon
Ordered by: US Air Force (26 AC-119G 'Shadow' and 26 AC-119K 'Stinger')

FAIRCHILD REPUBLIC F-105 THUNDERCHIEF (USA)

First flight 1955

Single-seat tactical fighter-bomber (F-105D) and two-seat operational trainer (F-105F) and ground defence suppression aircraft (F-105G)

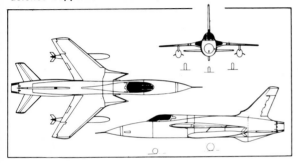

Photo and Drawing: F-105D Thunderchief

Data: F-105F Thunderchief
Power plant: One Pratt & Whitney J75-P-19W turbojet engine (26 500 lb; 12 030 kg st with water injection and afterburning)
Wing span: 34 ft 11·2 in (10·65 m)
Length overall: 69 ft 1·18 in (21·06 m)
Max T-O weight: 54 000 lb (24 495 kg)
Max level speed at 38 000 ft (11 600 m): 1 289 knots (1 485 mph; 2 390 km/h)

Max level speed at S/L: 826 knots (952 mph; 1 532 km/h)
Rate of climb at S/L: 32 000 ft (9 750 m)/min
Range with max fuel: 1 797 nm (2 070 miles; 3 330 km)
Armament: One General Electric M-61 Vulcan automatic multi-barrel 20 mm gun in port side of nose. Typical alternative loads are: (1) 650 gal centre-line tank, 450 gal tank on one inner wing pylon, nuclear store on other inner pylon; (2) 650 gal centre-line tank and four GAM-83B Bullpup nuclear missiles; (3) 450 gal tanks on centre-line and inner wing pylons, nuclear weapon in bomb bay; (4) 650 gal centre-line tank, two 3 000 lb bombs on inner wing pylons; (5) 650 gal centre-line tank, two 450 gal tanks on inner wing pylons, four Sidewinder missiles on outer wing pylons; (6) three rocket packs on centre-line, two on each inner wing pylon and one on each outer pylon; (7) nine BLU-1/B fire-bombs or nine MLU-10/B mines in similar arrangement to rocket packs, or sixteen leaflet bombs, 750 lb bombs, or MC-1 toxic bombs. Typical armament for the F-105G would comprise four Shrike missiles or two AGM-78B Standard ARMs. Adaptation of the F-105 to carry the latest missiles was continuing in 1972.
Ordered by: US Air Force (610 F-105D, including approx 30 with 'T-Stick II' bombing system, 143 F-105F, and unknown number of F-105G converted from F)

85

FAIREY (WESTLAND) GANNET (UK)

Three-seat airborne early warning aircraft (AEW Mk 3)

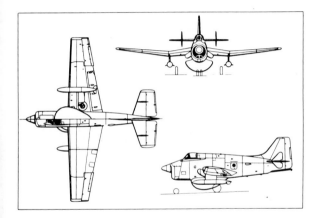

Data: AEW Mk 3
Power plant: One Bristol Siddeley Double Mamba 102 turboprop engine (3 875 ehp)
Wing span: 54 ft 6 in (16·61 m)
Length overall: 44 ft 0 in (13·41 m)
Max T-O weight: approx 24 000 lb (10 885 kg)
Max level speed at 5 000 ft (1 525 m): approx 217 knots (250 mph; 402 km/h)
Range: approx 695 nm (800 miles; 1 285 km)
Ordered by: Royal Navy (38 AEW Mk 3)

FMA IA 58 PUCARÁ (Argentina)

First flight 1969

Tandem two-seat counter-insurgency aircraft

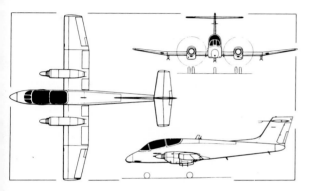

Data: Production version
Power plant: Two Turboméca Astazou XVIG turbo-prop engines (each 1 022 ehp)
Wing span: 47 ft 6¾ in (14·50 m)
Length overall: 46 ft 3 in (14·10 m)
Max T-O weight: 14 300 lb (6 486 kg)
Max level speed at 9 840 ft (3 000 m): 281 knots (323 mph; 520 km/h)
Rate of climb at S/L: 3 543 ft (1 080 m)/min
Service ceiling at 13 668 lb (6 200 kg) AUW: 27 165 ft (8 280 m)
Range with max fuel at 16 400 ft (5 000 m): 1 641 nm (1 890 miles; 3 042 km)
Armament: Two 20 mm Hispano cannon and four 7·62 mm FN machine-guns in fuselage. One attachment point beneath centre of fuselage and one beneath each wing outboard of engine nacelle for a variety of external stores, including auxiliary fuel tanks
Ordered by: Argentine Air Force (five pre-series and 30 production aircraft)

GENERAL DYNAMICS F-111 (USA)

First flight 1964

Side-by-side two-seat tactical fighter-bomber

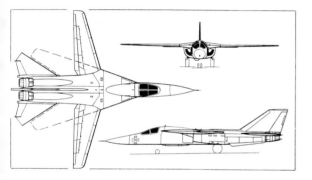

Photo: F-111F
Drawing: F-111A

Data: F-111A (F-111C has wing span of 70 ft 0 in; 21·34 m/33 ft 11 in; 10·34 m)
Power plant: Two Pratt and Whitney TF30-P-3 turbofan engines (each 21 000 lb; 9 525 kg st with afterburning)
Wing span:
spread: 63 ft 0 in (19·20 m)
fully swept: 31 ft 11·4 in (9·74 m)
Length overall: 73 ft 6 in (22·40 m)
Max T-O weight: 91 500 lb (41 500 kg)
Max level speed at height: 1 433 knots (1 650 mph; 2 655 km/h)
Max level speed at S/L: 794 knots (915 mph; 1 472 km/h)
Service ceiling: over 60 000 ft (18 300 m)
Range with max internal fuel: over 3 300 nm (3 800 miles; 6 100 km)
Armament: External stores are carried on four attachments under each wing, for a wide range of conventional and nuclear weapons, including the latest air-to-surface tactical weapons. Fuselage weapon bay for bombs or a 20 mm M-61A1 multi-barrel cannon
Ordered by: Air forces of Australia (24 F-111C) and USA (Air Force, 139 F-111A, 96 F-111D, 94 F-111E and 94 F-111F)

GENERAL DYNAMICS FB-111A (USA)

First flight 1967

Side-by-side two-seat strategic bomber

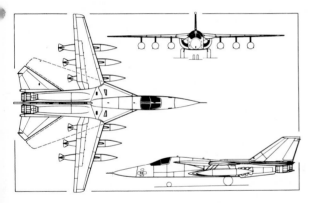

Power plant: Two Pratt and Whitney TF30-P-7 turbofan engines (each approx 20 000 lb; 9 070 kg st with afterburning)

Wing span:
spread: 70 ft 0 in (21·34 m)
fully swept: 33 ft 11 in (10·34 m)

Length overall: 73 ft 6 in (22·40 m)

Max T-O weight: approx 100 000 lb (45 360 kg)

Max level speed at height: 1 433 knots (1 650 mph; 2 655 km/h)

Max level speed at S/L: 794 knots (915 mph; 1 472 km/h)

Tactical radius: approx 1 085 nm (1 250 miles; 2 010 km)

Armament: Max load 50 × 750 lb bombs, of which two are carried in internal bay and 48 in twin clusters of three on eight underwing attachments. Full load is carried with wings swept at 26°, reducing to 38 bombs (six underwing attachments) at 54° of sweep, or 20 bombs at full sweep. Ability to carry six AGM-69A SRAM missiles

Ordered by: US Air Force (76)

GENERAL DYNAMICS YF-16 (USA)

Single-seat lightweight fighter

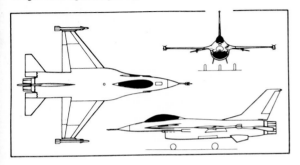

Power plant: One Pratt and Whitney F100-PW-100 turbofan engine (in the 25 000 lb; 11 340 kg thrust class with afterburning)

Wing span: 30 ft 0 in (9·14 m)

Length overall: 47 ft 0 in (14·32 m)

Max T-O weight:
with full internal fuel, two IR missiles and 500 rounds of ammunition for the M-61 gun: 17 500 lb (7 938 kg)

Armament: One fuselage-mounted M-61 20 mm multi-barrel cannon, and an infra-red missile mounted on each wingtip. Hardpoints for the carriage of underwing stores, including auxiliary fuel tanks or ECM pods

Ordered by: US Air Force (2 prototypes for competitive evaluation in 1974 against Northrop YF-17)

GRUMMAN A-6 INTRUDER (USA)

First flight 1960

Side-by-side two-seat carrier-borne strike (A-6), electronic reconnaissance (EA-6) and tanker aircraft (KA-6)

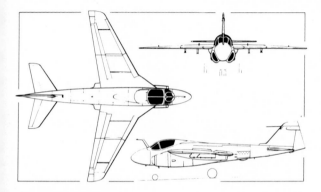

Photo: A-6E Intruder
Drawing: A-6A Intruder

Data: A-6A Intruder
Power plant: Two Pratt and Whitney J52-P-8A turbojet engines (each 9 300 lb; 4 218 kg st)
Wing span: 53 ft 0 in (16·15 m)
Length overall: 54 ft 7 in (16·64 m)
Max T-O weight: 60 626 lb (27 500 kg)
Max level speed at S/L: 595 knots (685 mph; 1 100 km/h)
Ferry range: 2 800 nm (3 225 miles; 5 190 km)
Armament: Five weapon attachment points, one under fuselage and two under each wing each have a 3 600 lb (1 633 kg) capacity. Typical weapon loads are 30 × 500 lb bombs in clusters of three, or two Bullpup missiles and three 2 000 lb general-purpose bombs
Ordered by: US Navy/Marine Corps (488 A-6A, of which 19 converted to A-6B, 12 to A-6C, 51 to KA-6D, 27 to EA-6A and 36 to A-6E)
See also Grumman EA-6B Prowler

GRUMMAN E-2 HAWKEYE (USA)

First flight 1960

Carrier-borne airborne early warning and fighter control
aircraft

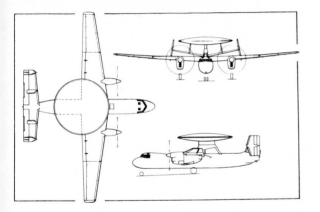

Photo and Drawing: E-2B Hawkeye

Data: E-2C Hawkeye
Power plant: Two Allison T56-A-8/8B turboprop
  engines (each 4 050 ehp)
Wing span: 80 ft 7 in (24·56 m)
Length overall: 57 ft 7 in (17·55 m)
Max T-O weight: 51 490 lb (23 355 kg)
Max level speed: over 315 knots (363 mph; 584
  km/h)
Service ceiling: 28 100 ft (8 565 m)
Ferry range: 1 496 nm (1 722 miles; 2 771 km)
Ordered by: US Navy (59 E-2A/B and 11 E-2C)

GRUMMAN EA-6B PROWLER (USA)

Four-seat ECM/strike aircraft

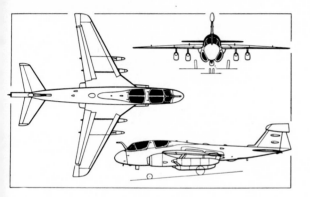

Power plant: Two Pratt and Whitney J52-P-8A turbojet engines (each 9 300 lb; 4 218 kg st)
Wing span: 53 ft 0 in (16·15 m)
Length overall: 59 ft 5 in (18·11 m)
Max T-O weight: 58 500 lb (26 535 kg)
Performance: Generally similar to A-6A Intruder (which see)
Ordered by: US Navy (44)

GRUMMAN F-14 TOMCAT (USA)

First flight 1970

Tandem two-seat carrier-borne air superiority and general-purpose fighter

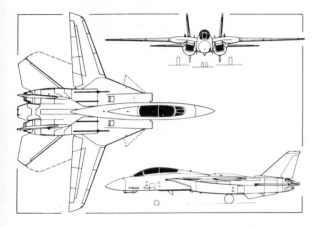

Data: F-14A
Power plant: Two Pratt and Whitney TF30-P-412 turbofan engines (each 20 600 lb; 9 344 kg st with afterburning)
Wing span:
unswept: 64 ft 1·5 in (19·54 m)
swept: 38 ft 2 in (11· 63 m)
Length overall: 61 ft 10·6 in (18·86 m)
Max T-O weight: 66 200 lb (30 028 kg)
Max level speed: over Mach 2 (1 146 knots; 1 320 mph; 2 125 km/h at altitude)
Armament: One General Electric M61-A1 Vulcan multi-barrel 20 mm gun mounted in the port side of forward fuselage. Four Sparrow air-to-air missiles mounted partially submerged in the under-fuselage. Two wing pylons, one under each fixed wing section, will carry both drop-tanks and four Sidewinder missiles, the latter being mounted one on either side of each pylon. For Phoenix and later missiles, Grumman has developed a concept in which removable pallets can be attached to the present Sparrow missile positions, the missiles then being attached to the pallets
Ordered by: US Navy (12 development aircraft and 122 F-14A; planned procurement of 313 aircraft altogether, including later F-14B)

GRUMMAN OV-1 MOHAWK (USA)

Side-by-side two-seat observation aircraft

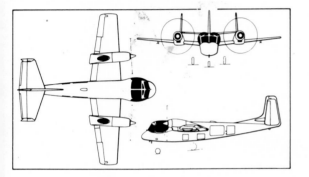

Photo: OV-1B Mohawk
Drawing: OV-1A Mohawk

Data: OV-1D Mohawk
Power plant: Two Lycoming T53-L-701 turboprop engines (each 1 400 shp)
Wing span: 48 ft 0 in (14·63 m)
Length overall: 41 ft 0 in (12·50 m)
Max T-O weight:
 SLAR: 18 109 lb (8 214 kg)
 IR: 17 912 lb (8 124 kg)
Max level speed at 10 000 ft (3 050 m), 40% fuel:
 SLAR: 251 knots (289 mph; 465 km/h)
 IR: 265 knots (305 mph; 491 km/h)
Max rate of climb at S/L:
 SLAR: 3 466 ft (1 056 m)/min
 IR: 3 618 ft (1 102 m)/min
Service ceiling: 25 000 ft (7 620 m)
Max range with external tanks at 20 000 ft (6 100 m):
 SLAR: 820 nm (944 miles; 1 520 km)
 IR: 878 nm (1 011 miles; 1 627 km)
Equipment: Photo surveillance system consists of two KA-60C 180-degree panoramic camera systems and one KA-76 serial frame camera. Infra-red AN/AAS-24 surveillance system. Alternative AN/APS-94D side-looking airborne radar (SLAR) system. ECM pods and an LS-59A photo-flash unit can be carried on underwing stations
Ordered by: US Army (more than 375 OV-1A/B/C/D, including 36 OV-1A)

GRUMMAN S-2 TRACKER and E-1 TRACER (USA)

First flights 1952/1958

Four-seat carrier-borne anti-submarine attack (Tracker) and airborne early warning aircraft (Tracer)

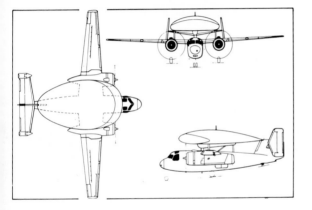

Photo: S-2E Tracker
Drawing: E-1B Tracer

Data: S-2E Tracker
Power plant: Two Wright R-1820-82WA piston engines (each 1 525 hp)
Wing span: 72 ft 7 in (22·13 m)
Length overall: 43 ft 6 in (13·26 m)
Max T-O weight: 29 150 lb (13 222 kg)
Max level speed at S/L: 230 knots (265 mph; 426 km/h)
Service ceiling: 21 000 ft (6 400 m)
Ferry range: 1 128 nm (1 300 miles; 2 095 km)
Armament: Fuselage holding 60 echo-sounding depth charges. One Mk 101 or Mk 57 nuclear depth bomb or equivalent store in bomb bay. Six underwing pylons for torpedoes, 5 in rockets, etc; 32 sonobuoys in nacelles.
Ordered by: Air forces of Argentine (Navy 6 S-2A), Australia (Navy 14 S-2E), Brazil (13 S-2A/CS2F-1), Canada (43 CS2F-1 and 57 CS2F-2/3), Italy (48 S-2A), Japan (Navy 60 S-2A), Netherlands (Navy 24 S-2A/N), Taiwan (9 S-2A), Thailand (S-2A), Turkey (12 S-2E and 2 TS-2A), Uruguay (3 S-2A) and USA (Navy more than 500 S-2A/TS-2A/US-2A/ S-2B/US-2B/S-2F, 60 S-2C/US-2C/RS-2C, 121 S-2D and 87 C-1A Trader transport equivalents, 227 S-2E and 88 E-1B Tracer)

HANDLEY PAGE VICTOR (UK)

First flight 1952

Flight refuelling tanker and strategic reconnaissance aircraft

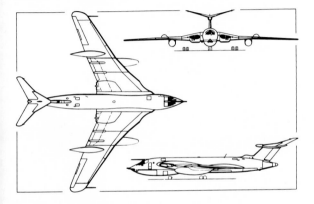

Photo: Victor K Mk 1A
Drawing: Victor SR Mk 2

Data: Victor K Mk 2 tanker
Power plant: Four Rolls-Royce Conway RCo.17 Mk 201 turbojet engines (each 20 600 lb; 9 344 kg st)
Wing span: 120 ft 0 in (36·58 m)
Length overall: 114 ft 11 in (35·03 m)
Max T-O weight: over 170 000 lb (77 110 kg)
Max level speed at 40 000 ft (12 190 m): over 521 knots (600 mph; 965 km/h)
Service ceiling: Over 60 000 ft (18 300 m)
Max range: 3 995 nm (4 600 miles; 7 400 km)
Ordered by: Royal Air Force (total of approx 120, from which approx 20 K Mk 1A and approx 40 SR Mk 2/K Mk 2 remain in service)

HAWKER HUNTER (UK)

First flight 1951

Single-seat fighter, ground attack and reconnaissance aircraft and side-by-side two-seat trainer

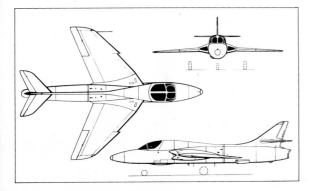

Photo: Hunter F(GA) Mk 9
Drawing: Hunter T Mk 7

Data: Hunter F(GA) Mk 9
Power plant: One Rolls-Royce Avon Mk 207 turbojet engine (10 000 lb; 4 540 kg st)

Wing span: 33 ft 8 in (10·26 m)
Length overall: 45 ft 10½ in (13·98 m)
Max T-O weight: 24 000 lb (10 885 kg)
Max level speed at S/L: 616 knots (710 mph; 1 142 km/h)
Rate of climb at S/L: approx 8 000 ft (2 440 m)/min
Service ceiling: 50 000 ft (15 250 m)
Range with external tanks: 1 595 nm (1 840 miles; 2 965 km)
Armament: Four 30 mm cannon in nose. On the inboard wing pylons two 1 000 lb bombs, two 500 lb bombs, two clusters of 12 × 3 in rockets, or two packs each containing 37 × 2 in rockets; 24 × 3 in rockets on outboard pylons
Ordered by: Air forces of Abu Dhabi (10 FGA Mk 76/FR Mk 76A and 2 T Mk 76A), Chile (22 FGA Mk 71 and 3 T Mk 7), Denmark (30 F Mk 51, 4 T Mk 7 and 2 T Mk 53), India (196 FGA Mk 56 and 34 T Mk 66), Iraq (37 FGA Mk 59, 4 FR Mk 10 and 9 T Mk 69), Jordan (22 FGA Mk 73 and 3 T Mk 66B), Kuwait (4 FGA Mk 57 and 2 T Mk 67), Lebanon (5 F Mk 6, 5 FB Mk 9 and 2 T Mk 69), Peru (16 F Mk 52 and 1 T Mk 62), Rhodesia (12 FGA Mk 9), Saudi Arabia (4 FGA Mk 9 and 2 T Mk 66), Singapore (12 FGA Mk 74, 4 FR Mk 74A and 4 T Mk 75), Switzerland (150 F Mk 58) and UK (Air Force more than 55 T Mk 7 and 30 FGA Mk 9 remaining in service; Navy 40 T Mk 8 and 25 GA Mk 11)

HAWKER SIDDELEY BUCCANEER (UK)

Tandem two-seat carrier-borne and land-based low-level strike aircraft

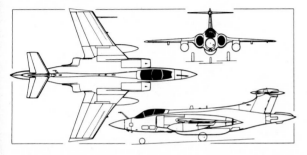

Photo and Drawing: Buccaneer S Mk 2B

Data: Buccaneer S Mk 2A/2B
Power plant: Two Rolls-Royce RB 168-1A Spey Mk 101 turbofan engines (each 11 100 lb; 5 035 kg st)
Wing span: 44 ft 0 in (13·41 m)

Length overall: 63 ft 5 in (19·33 m)
Max T-O weight: 62 000 lb (28 123 kg)
Max design level speed at 200 ft (61 m): 560 knots (645 mph; 1 038 km/h)
Typical strike range: 2 000 nm (2 300 miles; 3 700 km)
Armament: Rotating weapons bay door can carry four 1 000 lb HE Mk 10 bombs, a 440 Imp gallon (2 000 litre) fuel tank, or a reconnaissance pack. Each of the four wing pylon stations can be adapted to carry a wide variety of external stores. Typical loads for any one pylon include one 1 000 lb HE Mk N1 or Mk 10 bomb; two 500 lb or 540 lb bombs on tandem carriers; one 18-tube 68 mm rocket pod; one 36-tube 2 in rocket pod; 3 in rockets; or an HSD/Matra Martel air-to-surface missile. Each pylon is also suitable for carrying three 1 000 lb stores on triple release ejection units, or six 500 lb stores on multiple ejection release units, with only small restrictions on the flight envelope. Max internal and external stores load is 16 000 lb (7 257 kg)
Ordered by: Air forces of South Africa (16 S Mk 50) and UK (approx 80 S Mk 2A/2B for Air Force and S Mk 2C/D for Navy, converted from S Mk 2, and 42 new-production S Mk 2B for Air Force only)

HAWKER SIDDELEY GNAT and GNAT TRAINER (UK)

First flights 1955/1959

Single-seat lightweight fighter (Mk 1) and tandem two-seat trainer (T Mk 1)

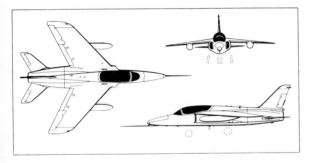

Photo: Gnat Mk 1 built by HAL, India
Drawing: Gnat T Mk 1

Data: Gnat Mk 1
Power plant: One Bristol Siddeley Orpheus 701 (BOr 2) turbojet engine (4 520 lb; 2 050 kg st)
Wing span: 22 ft 2 in (6·75 m)
Length overall: 29 ft 9 in (9.06 m)
Interceptor version; T-O weight: 6 650 lb (3 010 kg)
Tactical version; max T-O weight with external tanks and armament: 8 885 lb (4 020 kg)
Max level speed at 20 000 ft (6 100 m): 603 knots (695 mph; 1 118 km/h)
Climb to 45 000 ft (13 700 m): 5 min 15 sec
Service ceiling: Over 50 000 ft (15 250 m)
Radius of action with external tanks: 434 nm (500 miles; 805 km)
Armament: Two 30 mm Aden cannon in the air intake fairings, one on each side of fuselage. Provision for underwing mounting of two 500 lb bombs or 12 × 3 in rocket projectiles, etc
Ordered by: Air forces of Finland (12 Mk 1), India (over 240 Mk 1)*, and UK (105 T Mk 1)
*India has Mk 2 fighter under development

HAWKER SIDDELEY HARRIER (UK)

Single-seat V/STOL strike/reconnaissance aircraft (GR Mks 1/1A/3 and AV-8A) and tandem two-seat operational trainer (T Mks 2/2A/4 and TAV-8A)

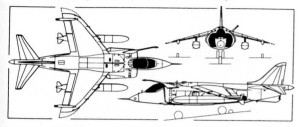

Photo: AV-8A Harrier of the USMC
Drawing: Harrier GR Mk 1
Data: Harrier GR Mk 1A
Power plant: GR Mk 1A/T Mk 2A and early AV-8As each have one Rolls-Royce Bristol Pegasus Mk 102 (20 000 lb; 9 071 kg st) vectored-thrust turbofan engine; GR Mk 3/T Mk 4 and later AV-8As have Pegasus Mk 103 (21 500 lb; 9 752 kg st); these engines replace Pegasus Mk 101 (19 000 lb; 8 620 kg st) fitted originally in GR Mk 1 and T Mk 2; all AV-8As will eventually have Pegasus Mk 103

Wing span:
combat: 25 ft 3 in (7·70 m)
ferry: 29 ft 8 in (9·04 m)

Length overall: 45 ft 6 in (13·87 m)
Max T-O weight: over 25 000 lb (11 339 kg)

Speed at low altitude: over 640 knots (737 mph; 1 186 km/h) EAS
Mach number (in a dive): approaching 1·3
Ceiling: over 50 000 ft (15 250 m)
Range with one in-flight refuelling: over 3 000 nm (3 455 miles; 5 560 km)
Ferry range, unrefuelled: approaching 2 000 nm (2 300 miles; 3 700 km)
Armament: All weapons carried on one under-fuselage and four underwing pylons, all with ML ejector release units. Inboard wing points and fuselage point are stressed for loads of up to 2 000 lb (910 kg) each, and outboard underwing pair for loads of up to 650 lb (295 kg) each; the two strake fairings under the fuselage can each be replaced by a 30 mm Aden gun pod and ammunition. The Harrier is cleared for operations with a maximum external load exceeding 5 000 lb (2 270 kg), but has flown with a weapon load of 8 000 lb (3 630 kg) It can carry 30 mm guns, bombs, rockets and flares of UK and US designs, and in addition to its fixed reconnaissance camera can also carry a five-camera reconnaissance pod on the under-fuselage pylon. A typical combat load comprises a pair of 30 mm Aden gun pods, a 1 000 lb bomb on the under-fuselage pylon, a 1 000 lb bomb on each of the inboard underwing pylons, and a Matra 155 launcher with 19 × 68 mm SNEB rockets on each outboard underwing pylon
Ordered by: Air forces of UK (92 GR Mks 1/1A/3 and 15 T Mks 2/2A/4) and USA (Marine Corps 102 AV-8A and 8 TAV-8A)

HAWKER SIDDELEY NIMROD (UK)

First flight 1967

Long-range anti-submarine and maritime reconnaissance aircraft

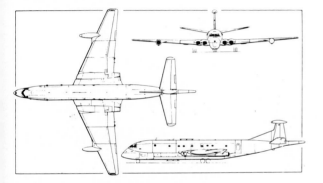

Photo and Drawing: Nimrod MR Mk 1

Data: Nimrod MR Mk 1
Power plant: Four Rolls-Royce RB 168 Spey Mk 250 turbofan engines (each approx 11 500 lb; 5 217 kg st)
Wing span: 114 ft 10 in (35·00 m)
Length overall: 126 ft 9 in (38·63 m)
Typical T-O weights: 175 500 lb (79 605 kg) to 192 000 lb (87 090 kg)
Max speed for operational necessity, ISA+20°C: 500 knots (575 mph; 926 km/h)
Typical ferry range: 4 500-5 000 nm (5 180-5 755 miles; 8 340-9 265 km)
Armament and equipment: Bay for active and passive sonobuoys. Ventral weapons bay can accommodate full range of ASW weapons including bombs, mines, depth charges and torpedoes. Pylon beneath each wing at approx one-third span, on which can be carried AS.12 or other weapons as required. ASW equipment includes SONICS 1C sonar and a new long-range sonar system. ASV 21 air-to-surface-vessel detection radar, Autolycus ionisation detector, and ECM gear. MAD (magnetic anomaly detector) in extended tail 'sting'. Searchlight in starboard external wing fuel tank
Ordered by: Royal Air Force (46 MR Mk 1 and 3 R Mk 1)

HAWKER SIDDELEY (AVRO) SHACKLETON AEW Mk 2 (UK)

First flight 1971

Airborne early warning aircraft

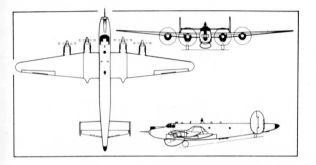

Photo and Drawing: Shackleton AEW Mk 2

Data: Shackleton AEW Mk 2
Power plant: Four Rolls-Royce Griffon 57A piston engines (each 2 455 hp)
Wing span: 119 ft 10 in (36·52 m)
Length overall: 87 ft 4 in (26·62 m)
Max level speed: 152 knots (175 mph; 282 km/h)
Range: 2 515 nm (2 900 miles; 4 665 km)
Ordered by: Royal Air Force (12, converted from MR Mk 2)

HAWKER SIDDELEY VULCAN (UK)

Medium attack and tactical support bomber

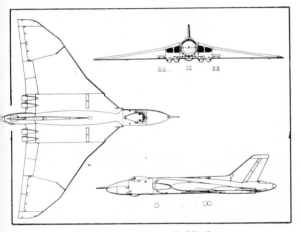

Photo and Drawing: Vulcan B Mk 2

Data: Vulcan B Mk 2
Power plant: Four Rolls-Royce Bristol Olympus Mk 301 turbojet engines (each 20 000 lb; 9 072 kg st)
Wing span: 111 ft 0 in (33·83 m)
Length overall: 99 ft 11 in (30·45 m)
Max T-O weight: over 180 000 lb (81 645 kg)
Max cruising speed, at 50 000 ft (15 240 m): over 542 knots (625 mph; 1 005 km/h)
Max cruising height: 55 000 ft (16 750 m)
Combat radius:
at high and low altitude: 1 500 nm (1 725 miles; 2 780 km)
at high altitude: 1 995 nm (2 300 miles; 3 700 km)
with flight refuelling: 2 495 nm (2 875 miles; 4 630 km)
Armament: Weapon load can include a Hawker Siddeley Blue Steel air-to-surface missile, free-fall nuclear weapons or 21 × 1 000 lb HE bombs
Ordered by: Royal Air Force (approx 100 B Mk 2)

HINDUSTAN HF-24 MARUT (India)

Single-seat ground attack fighter

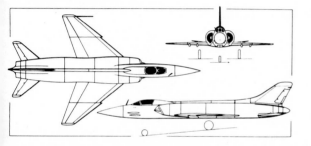

Photo and Drawing: HF-24 Marut Mk I

Data: HF-24 Mk I
Power plant: Two HAL-built Rolls-Royce Bristol Orpheus 703 turbojet engines (each 4 850 lb; 2 200 kg st)
Wing span: 29 ft 6¼ in (9·00 m)
Length overall: 52 ft 0¾ in (15·87 m)
Max T-O weight:
 early aircraft, without extended chord: 24 085 lb (10 925 kg)
 later aircraft, with extended chord: 24 048 lb (10 908 kg)
Max level speed at 40 000 ft (12 200 m): 584 knots (673 mph; 1 083 km/h)
Max permissible speed at S/L: 620 knots (714 mph; 1 149 km/h)
Armament: Four 30 mm Aden Mk 2 guns in nose and retractable pack of 50 SNEB 68 mm air-to-air rockets in lower fuselage aft of nosewheel unit. Attachments for four 1 000 lb bombs, napalm tanks, Type 116 SNEB rocket packs, clusters of T10 air-to-surface rockets, drop-tanks or other stores under wings
Ordered by: Indian Air Force (80, including 12 of 18 pre-production aircraft built)

ILYUSHIN Il-28 (USSR)

NATO Code Name *Beagle*
Four-seat tactical bomber, reconnaissance and ECM aircraft

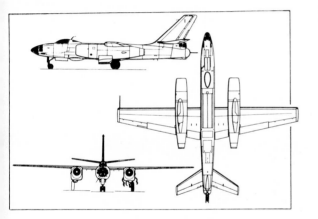

Power plant: Two Klimov VK-1 turbojet engines (each 5 950 lb; 2 700 kg st)
Wing span: 70 ft 4½ in (21·45 m)
Length of fuselage: 57 ft 11 in (17·65 m)
Max T-O weight: 46 297 lb (21 000 kg)
Max level speed at 14 765 ft (4 500 m): 485 knots (559 mph; 900 km/h)
Time to 32 800 ft (10 000 m): 18 min
Service ceiling: 41 000 ft (12 500 m)
Range with max bomb load: 1 219 nm (1 404 miles; 2 260 km)
Armament: Two 20 mm cannon in lower part of nose. Two 23 mm cannon in tail turret. Bomb load of 4 500 lb (2 040 kg)
Ordered by: Air forces of Afghanistan, Algeria, China, Czechoslovakia, Egypt, Finland, Germany (Democratic Republic), Hungary, Indonesia (Air Force and Navy), Iraq, North Korea, Morocco, Nigeria, Poland, Syria, USSR, North Vietnam and Yemen

Photo: Il-28 torpedo bomber

ILYUSHIN Il-38 (USSR)

First flight about 1971

NATO Code Name *May*
Anti-submarine and maritime patrol aircraft

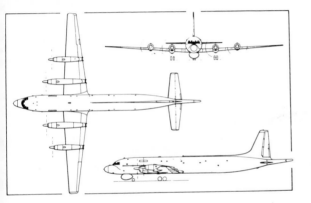

Power plant: Four Ivchenko AI-20M turboprop
engines (each 4 250 ehp)
Wing span: 122 ft 8½ in (37·40 m)
Length overall: 131 ft 0 in (39·92 m)
Max T-O weight: approx 140 000 lb (63 500 kg)
**Max continuous cruising speed at 15 000 ft
(4 575 m):** approx 347 knots (400 mph; 645 km/h)
Max range: approx 3 900 nm (4 500 miles; 7 240 km)
Equipment: Under-nose radome, MAD tail 'sting',
other specialised electronic equipment and a weapon-
carrying capability
Ordered by: Soviet Navy

KAMAN H-2 SEASPRITE (USA)

Utility (UH-2), armed rescue (HH-2) and anti-submarine helicopter (SH-2)

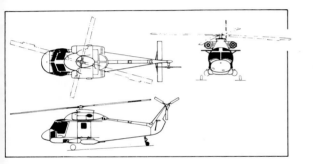

Photo: SH-2D Seasprite
Drawing: UH-2C Seasprite

Data: SH-2D Seasprite
Power plant: Two General Electric T58-GE-8F turboshaft engines (each 1 350 shp)
Main rotor diameter: 44 ft 0 in (13·41 m)
Length overall: 52 ft 7 in (16·03 m) blades turning
Overload T-O weight: 12 800 lb (5 805 kg)
Max level speed at S/L: 146 knots (168 mph; 270 km/h)
Max rate of climb at S/L: 2 440 ft (744 m)/min
Service ceiling: 22 500 ft (6 858 m)
Normal range with max fuel: 387 nm (445 miles; 716 km)
Armament and equipment: Hard mounts for MK-46 homing torpedoes. High-power search radar, sono-buoys, magnetic anomaly detector, associated electronic monitors and controls, smoke markers and flares
Ordered by: US Navy (88 UH-2A and 102 UH-2B, from which approx 60 converted to UH-2C, 6 to HH-2C, 50 to HH-2D, 20 to SH-2D and 2 to YSH-2E; planned eventually to convert all existing Seasprites to SH-2D/F configuration)

KAMOV Ka-25 (USSR)

NATO Code Name *Hormone*
Anti-submarine search and strike helicopter

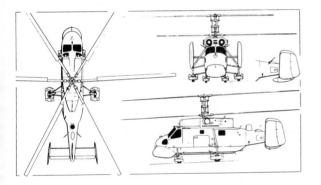

Power plant: Two Glushenkov GTD-3 turboshaft engines (each 900 shp)
Rotor diameter (each): 51 ft 8 in (15·74 m)
Length overall: 32 ft 0 in (9.75 m)
Max T-O weight: 16 100 lb (7 300 kg)
Max level speed: 119 knots (137 mph; 220 km/h)
Service ceiling: 11 500 ft (3 500 m)
Range with max fuel, with reserves: 351 nm (405 miles; 650 km)
Armament and equipment: External rack for small stores on each side of the fuselage. Doors under the fuselage enclose a weapons-bay for ASW torpedoes and other stores. Dipping sonar housed in compartment at rear of main cabin, immediately forward of tail-boom, and search radar under nose of anti-submarine version. Some aircraft have a blister fairing over equipment mounted at the base of the centre tail-fin; others have a cylindrical housing, with a transparent top, above the central point of the tail-boom, with shallow blister fairing to the rear of this
Ordered by: Soviet Navy

KAWASAKI P-2J (Japan)

First flight 1966

Anti-submarine and maritime patrol bomber

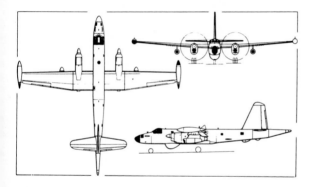

Power plant: Two General Electric T64-IHI-10 turboprop engines (each 2 850 ehp). Outboard of these, on underwing pylons, are two pod-mounted Ishikawajima J3-IHI-7C turbojets (each 3 085 lb; 1 400 kg st)

Wing span: 97 ft 8½ in (29·78 m)
Length overall: 95 ft 10¾ in (29·23 m)
Max T-O weight: 75 000 lb (34 019 kg)
Max cruising speed: 217 knots (250 mph; 402 km/h)
Max rate of climb at S/L: 1 800 ft (550 m)/min
Service ceiling: 30 000 ft (9 150 m)
Range with max fuel: 2 400 nm (2 765 miles; 4 450 km)
Equipment: APS-80J search radar. Details of operational equipment are classified, but this is of comparable standard to that carried by the Lockheed P-3 Orion and includes a smoke detector and MAD in the elongated tailcone. Searchlight in starboard wingtip pod
Ordered by: Japan (Navy 46, of planned procurement of 91)

LOCKHEED F-104 STARFIGHTER (USA)

First flight 1954

Single-seat all-weather tactical strike and reconnaissance fighter

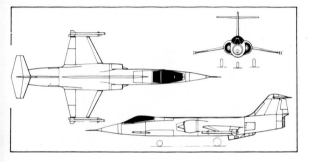

Photo: RF-104G Starfighter
Drawing: F-104G Starfighter
Data: F-104S Starfighter
Power plant: One General Electric J79-GE-19 turbojet engine (17 900 lb; 8 120 kg st with afterburning)
Wing span: 21 ft 11 in (6·68 m) without tip-tanks
Length overall: 54 ft 9 in (16·69 m)
Max T-O weight: 31 000 lb (14 060 kg)
Max level speed at 36 000 ft (11 000 m): 1 259 knots (1 450 mph; 2 330 km/h)

Service ceiling: 58 000 ft (17 680 m)
Radius with max fuel: 673 nm (775 miles; 1 247 km)
Ferry range, excluding flight refuelling: 1 576 nm (1 815 miles; 2 920 km)
Armament: Nine external attachment points, at wingtips, under wings and under fuselage, for bombs, rocket pods, auxiliary fuel tanks and Sidewinder air-to-air missiles. Normal primary armament consists of Raytheon Sparrow III air-to-air missiles and permanently installed M-61 20 mm rotary cannon in port underside of fuselage. Provision for two Sidewinders under fuselage and either a Sidewinder or 170 US gallon (645 litre) fuel tank on each wingtip
Ordered by: Air forces of Belgium (100 F-104G), Canada (200 CF-104 and 38 CF-104D), Denmark (40 F-104G and 10 TF-104G), German Federal Republic (Air Force 30 F-104F, more than 700 F-104G, approx 100 RF-104G and 119 TF-104G; Navy approx 150 F-104G and some TF-104G), Greece (36 F-104G), Italy (155 F-104G, 165 F-104S and 28 TF-104G), Japan (210 F-104J and 20 F-104DJ), Jordan (36 F-104A and 2 F-104B), Netherlands (120 F-104G, 20 RF-104G and 18 TF-104G), Norway (29 F-104G and 2 TF-104G), Pakistan (14 F-104A and 2 F-104B), Spain (18 F-104G and 3 TF-104G), Taiwan (80 F-104G, 15 RF-104G and some TF-104G), Turkey (38 F-104G and some TF-104G) and USA (155 F-104A, 26 F-104B, 77 F-104C, 22 F-104D and 180 TF-104G)

LOCKHEED P-2 NEPTUNE (USA)

First flight 1945

Maritime patrol bomber

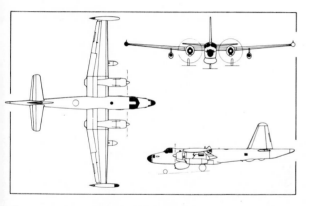

Photo: SP-2H Neptune
Drawing: P-2H Neptune

Data: P-2H Neptune
Power plant: Two Wright R-3350-32W piston engines (each 3 500 hp) and two Westinghouse J34 turbojet engines (each 3 400 lb; 1 540 kg st)
Wing span, with tip-tanks: 103 ft 10 in (31·65 m)
Length overall: 91 ft 8 in (27·94 m)
Max T-O weight: 79 895 lb (36 240 kg)
Max level speed: 350 knots (403 mph; 648 km/h)
Max level speed at 10 000 ft (3 050 m): 309 knots (356 mph; 573 km/h) with piston engines only
Service ceiling: 22 000 ft (6 700 m)
Max range with ferry tanks: 3 200 nm (3 685 miles; 5 930 km)
Armament: Provision for sixteen 5 in rocket projectiles under wings. Weapon load of 8 000 lb (3 630 kg), carried internally, may consist of bombs, depth charges or torpedoes. MAD gear and sonobuoy installation. Provision for optional dorsal turret with two 0·50 in machine-guns
Ordered by: Air forces of Argentine (Navy 6 P-2H), Australia (12 SP-2H), Brazil (14 P-2E), France (Navy 24 P-2H), Japan (Navy 76 P-2H*), Netherlands (Navy 17 SP-2H), Portugal (12 ex-Dutch SP-2E) and USA (Navy 424 P-2E, 83 P-2F and 359 P-2H)
See also Kawasaki P-2J

LOCKHEED P-3 ORION (USA)

Anti-submarine reconnaissance aircraft

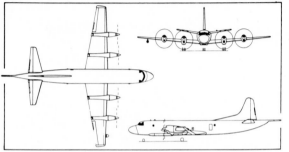

Photo: EP-3B Orion   **Drawing:** P-3B Orion
Data: P-3C Orion
Power plant: Four Allison T56-A-14 turboprop engines (each 4 910 ehp)
Wing span: 99 ft 8 in (30·37 m)
Length overall: 116 ft 10 in (35·61 m)
Max permissible weight: 142 000 lb (64 410 kg)
Max level speed at 15 000 ft (4 570 m):
 at AUW of 105 000 lb (47 625 kg): 411 knots (473 mph; 761 km/h)
Rate of climb at 1 500 ft (457 m): 1 950 ft (594 m)/min
Service ceiling: 28 300 ft (8 625 m)
Max mission radius, no time on station:
 at AUW of 135 000 lb (61 235 kg): 2 070 nm (2 383 miles; 3 835 km)

Mission radius, 3 hr on station:
 at 1 500 ft (457 m): 1 346 nm (1 550 miles; 2 494 km)

Armament: Bomb bay can accommodate a 2 000 lb MK-25/39/55/56 mine, three 1 000 lb MK-36/52 mines, three MK-57 depth charges, eight MK-54 depth bombs, eight MK-43/44/46 torpedoes or a combination of two MK-101 nuclear depth bombs and four MK-43/44/46 torpedoes. Ten underwing pylons for stores. Two under centre-section each side can carry torpedoes or 2 000 lb mines. Three under outer wing each side can carry respectively (inboard to outboard) a torpedo or 2 000 lb mine (or searchlight on starboard wing), a torpedo or 1 000 lb mine or rockets singly or in pods; a torpedo or 500 lb mine or rockets singly or in pods. Torpedoes can be carried underwing only for ferrying; mines can be carried and released. Sonobuoys are loaded and launched externally and internally. Max total weapon load includes six 2 000 lb mines under wings and a 7 252 lb (3 290 kg) internal load made up of two MK-101 depth bombs, four MK-44 torpedoes, pyrotechnic pistol and 12 signals, 87 sonobuoys, 42 MK-7 marine markers, two BT buoys and two MK-5 parachute flares

Ordered by: Air forces of Australia (10 P-3B), Iran (4 P-3C), New Zealand (5 P-3B), Norway (5 P-3B), Spain (3 P-3B) and USA (Navy 286 P-3A/WP-3A/P-3B, including 12 converted to EP-3E, and P-3C/RP-3D)

LOCKHEED S-3A VIKING (USA)

First flight 1972

Four-seat carrier-borne anti-submarine aircraft

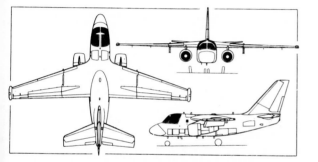

Power plant: Two General Electric TF34-GE-2 high by-pass ratio turbofan engines (each approx 9 000 lb; 4 082 kg st)
Wing span: 68 ft 8 in (20·93 m)
Length overall: 53 ft 4 in (16·26 m)
Normal ASW T-O weight: 42 500 lb (19 277 kg)

Max level speed: approx 440 knots (506 mph; 814 km/h)
Rate of climb at S/L: over 4 200 ft (1 280 m)/min
Service ceiling: above 35 000 ft (10 670 m)
Combat range: more than 2 000 nm (2 303 miles; 3 705 km)
Ferry range: more than 3 000 nm (3 454 miles; 5 558 km)
Armament: Split weapons bays equipped with BRU-14/A bomb rack assemblies can deploy four MK-36 destructors, four MK-46 torpedoes, four MK-82 bombs, two MK-57 or four MK-54 depth bombs, or four MK-53 mines. BRU-11/A bomb racks installed on the two wing pylons permit carriage of SUU-44/A flare launchers, MK-52, MK-55 or MK-56 mines, MK-20-2 cluster bombs, Aero 1D auxiliary fuel tanks, or two rocket pods of type LAU-68/A (7 FFAR 2·75 in), LAU-61/A (19 FFAR 2·75 in), LAU-69/A (19 FFAR 2·75 in), or LAU-10A/A (4 FFAR 5·0 in). Alternatively, installation of TER-7 triple ejector racks on the BRU-11/A bomb racks makes it possible to carry three rocket pods, flare launchers, MK-20 cluster bombs, MK-82 bombs, MK-36 destructors, or MK-76-5 or MK-106-4 practice bombs under each wing
Ordered by: US Navy (8 development aircraft and 40 production S-3A, of planned total procurement of 191 aircraft)

LOCKHEED SR-71A (USA)

Tandem two-seat long-range strategic reconnaissance aircraft

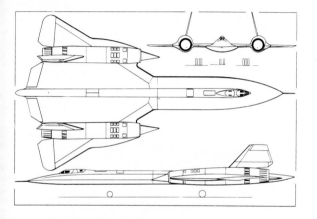

Photo and Drawing: SR-71A

Data: SR-71A except where indicated; weight and performance estimated

Power plant: Two Pratt and Whitney JT11D-20B (J58) turbojet engines (each 32 500 lb; 14 740 kg st with afterburning)

Wing span: 55 ft 7 in (16·95 m)

Length overall: 107 ft 5 in (32·74 m)

Max T-O weight: 170 000 lb (77 110 kg)

Max level speed, short periods only, YF-12A version: 2 005 knots (2 310 mph; 3 717 km/h)

Max speed, long-range cruising, YF-12A version: 1 720 knots (1 980 mph; 3 186 km/h)

Operational ceiling: over 80 000 ft (24 400 m)

Range, at Mach 3·0 at 78 750 ft (24 000 m): 2 590 nm (2 980 miles; 4 800 km)

Max endurance, at Mach 3·0 at 78 750 ft (24 000 m): 1 hr 30 min

Equipment: Internal equipment ranges from simple battlefield surveillance systems to multiple-sensor high-performance systems for interdiction reconnaissance and strategic systems capable of specialised surveillance of up to 60 000 sq miles (155 400 km²) of territory in one hour

Ordered by: US Air Force (approx 25, including small number of SR-71B/C trainers)

McDONNELL F-101 VOODOO (USA)

Tandem two-seat long-range interceptor fighter
(F/CF-101B) and single seat reconnaissance aircraft

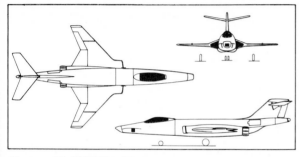

Photo: CF-101B Voodoo
Drawing: RF-101C Voodoo

Data: F-101B Voodoo
Power plant: Two Pratt and Whitney J57-P-55
   turbojet engines (each 14 880 lb; 6 750 kg st with
   afterburning)
Wing span: 39 ft 8 in (12·09 m)
Length overall: 67 ft 5 in (20·55 m)
Max T-O weight: 46 500 lb (21 090 kg)
Max level speed at 40 000 ft (12 200 m): 1 059
   knots (1 220 mph; 1 963 km/h)
Rate of climb at S/L: 14 000 ft (4 270 m)/min
Service ceiling: 52 000 ft (15 850 m)
Range: 1 345 nm (1 550 miles; 2 495 km)
Armament: Two Genie air-to-air missiles under
   fuselage and three Falcon air-to-air missiles carried
   internally
Ordered by: Air forces of Canada (66 CF-101B/CF-
   101F), Taiwan (25 RF-101A) and USA (50 F-101A/
   RF-101G, 47 F-101C/RF-101H, 166 RF-101C and
   478 F-101B/TF-101B)

McDONNELL DOUGLAS A-4 SKYHAWK (USA)

Single-seat carrier-borne light attack bomber

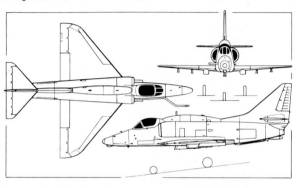

Photo and Drawing: A-4M Skyhawk

Data: A-4M Skyhawk
Power plant: One Pratt and Whitney J52-P-408A turbojet engine (11 200 lb; 5 080 kg st)
Wing span: 27 ft 6 in (8·38 m)
Length overall, excluding flight refuelling probe: 40 ft 3¼ in (12·27 m)

Max T-O weight: 24 500 lb (11 113 kg)
Max level speed:
with 4 000 lb (1 814 kg) bomb load: 560 knots (645 mph; 1 038 km/h)
Max rate of climb at S/L: 8 440 ft (2 572 m)/min
Max ferry range at max T-O weight, standard reserves: 1 785 nm (2 055 miles; 3 307 km)
Armament: Provision for several hundred variations of military load, carried externally on one under-fuselage rack, capacity 3 500 lb (1 588 kg); two inboard underwing racks, capacity of each 2 250 lb (1 020 kg); and two outboard underwing racks, capacity of each 1 000 lb (450 kg). Weapons that can be deployed include nuclear or HE bombs, air-to-surface and air-to-air rockets, Sidewinder infra-red missiles, Bullpup air-to-surface missiles, ground attack gun pods, torpedoes, countermeasures equipment, etc. Two 20 mm MK-12 cannon in wing roots standard. DEFA 30 mm cannon available optionally on international versions.
Ordered by: Air forces of Argentine (Air Force 50 A-4B/P, Navy 16 A-4B/Q), Australia (Navy 16 A-4G and 4 TA-4G), Israel (approx 265, including 43 A-4E, 188 A-4H, 24 A-4N and 10 TA-4H), New Zealand (10 A-4K and 4 TA-4K), Singapore (approx 40 A-4B) and USA (Navy/Marine Corps 499 A-4E, more than 139 TA-4F, 146 A-4F, TA-4J, A-4L (conversions of A-4C) and more than 70 A-4M)

McDONNELL DOUGLAS F-4 PHANTOM II (USA)

First flight 1958

Tandem two-seat multi-mission land- and carrier-based fighter, fighter-bomber and reconnaissance aircraft

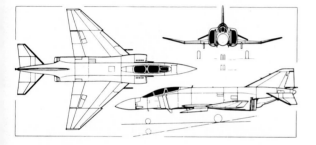

Photo: F-4J Phantom II
Drawing: FG Mk 1 (F-4K) Phantom

Data: F-4EJ Phantom
Power plant: Two Ishikawajima-Harima (General Electric) J79-IHI-17 turbojet engines (each 17 900 lb; 8 120 kg st with afterburning)
Wing span: 38 ft 5 in (11·71 m)
Length overall: 62 ft 11¾ in (19·20 m)
Max T-O weight: 57 400 lb (26 035 kg)
Max level speed at 36 000 ft (11 000 m): 1 262 knots (1 454 mph; 2 340 km/h)
Rate of climb at S/L: 49 500 ft (15 100 m)/min
Service ceiling: 58 050 ft (17 700 m)
Range: 1 600 nm (1 840 miles; 2 960 km)
Armament: Internally mounted M-61A1 20 mm multi-barrel gun. Launchers for Mitsubishi AAM-2 air-to-air missiles and Sparrow III missiles. Five attachments under wings and fuselage for stores
Ordered by: Air forces of German Federal Republic (88 RF-4E and 175 F-4F), Iran (144 F-4D/E), Israel (130 F-4E and 6 RF-4E), Japan (104 F-4EJ and 18 RF-4EJ), South Korea (18 F-4E), Spain (36 F-4C), UK (Air Force 120 FGR Mk 2 = F-4M; Navy 48 FG Mk 1 = F-4K) and USA (Air Force 583 F-4C, 481 RF-4C, 825 F-4D and many F-4E; Navy/Marine Corps 696 F-4A/B, 46 RF-4B, 12 F-4G, and F-4J)

Single-seat multi-purpose fighter

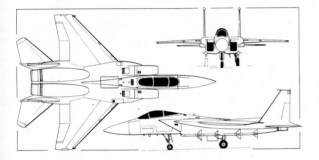

Photo and Drawing: F-15A Eagle

Data: F-15A Eagle

Power plant: Two Pratt and Whitney F100-PW-101 turbofan engines (each approx 29 000 lb; 13 155 kg st with afterburning)

Wing span: 42 ft 9¾ in (13·05 m)

Length overall: 63 ft 9¾ in (19·45 m)

Max level speed: over 1 146 knots (1 320 mph; 2 125 km/h)

Armament: Provision for carriage and launch of a variety of air-to-air weapons over short and medium ranges. One 20 mm M-61A1 six-barrel gun in initial production aircraft

Ordered by: US Air Force (18 F-15A and 2 two-seat TF-15 development aircraft; option held for 107 production aircraft, including 15 TF-15)

MARTIN and GENERAL DYNAMICS B-57 (USA)

Tandem two-seat light tactical bomber (B-57) and reconnaissance aircraft (RB-57)

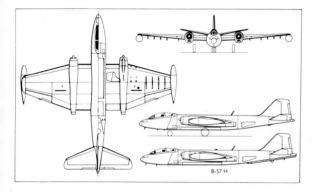

Data: RB-57F
Power plant: Two Pratt and Whitney TF33-P-11 turbofan engines (each 18 000 lb; 8 165 kg st), plus two Pratt and Whitney J60-P-9 auxiliary turbojet engines (each 3 300 lb; 1 500 kg st)
Wing span: 122 ft 5 in (37·32 m)
Length overall: 69 ft 0 in (21·03 m)
Equipment: Radar in the fuselage nose and unspecified electronics in the wingtips. Four underwing hardpoints for external stores, of which two are used normally to carry the auxiliary turbojets. When the turbojets are not required, all four hard-points are available for stores or equipment pods
Armament and equipment (B-57G): Capable of detecting, tracking and bombing a target in darkness. External changes from standard B-57 include a broad 'chin' fairing beneath the nose which houses much of the new equipment. A window on the port side is provided for a low-light-level TV camera and laser rangefinder, with a starboard window for infra-red equipment. Multi-function radar is housed in the nose.
Ordered by: Air forces of Pakistan (30 B-57B), Taiwan (2 RB-57D), USA (8 B-57A, 67 RB-57A, 202 B-57B/EB-57B, 38 B-57C, 20 RB-57D and 68 B-57E, from which 12 converted to RB-57F and 12 or more to B-57G), and South Vietnam (4 B-57B)
See also English Electric Canberra

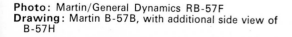

Photo: Martin/General Dynamics RB-57F
Drawing: Martin B-57B, with additional side view of B-57H

MIKOYAN/GUREVICH MiG-17 (USSR)

First flight about 1952

NATO Code Name *Fresco*
Single-seat fighter and ground attack aircraft

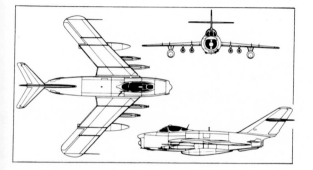

Photo: MiG -17F
Drawing: MiG-17PFU

Data: MiG-17F
Power plant: One Klimov VK-1A turbojet engine (7 450 lb; 3 380 kg st with afterburning)
Wing span: 31 ft 6 in (9·60 m)
Length overall: 37 ft $3\frac{1}{4}$ in (11·36 m)
Max T-O weight: 13 379 lb (6 069 kg)
Max level speed at 9 845 ft (3 000 m): 617 knots (711 mph; 1 145 km/h)
Rate of climb at S/L: 12 795 ft (3 900 m)/min
Service ceiling: 54 460 ft (16 600 m)
Max range, with external tanks and bombs: 755 nm (870 miles; 1 400 km)
Armament: One 37 mm N-37 and two 23 mm NR-23 cannon. Provision for four 8-rocket pods or a total of 1 100 lb (500 kg) of bombs beneath the wings
Ordered by: Air forces of Afghanistan, Albania, Algeria, Bulgaria, China, Cuba, Egypt, Germany (Democratic Republic), Guinea, Hungary, Indonesia, Iraq, Khmer, North Korea, Nigeria, Poland, Romania, Somalia, Sri Lanka, Syria, USSR, North Vietnam and Yemen

MIKOYAN MiG-19 (USSR)

NATO Code Name *Farmer*
Single-seat fighter and ground attack aircraft

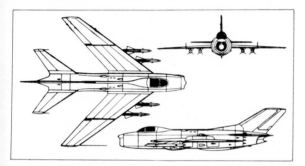

Photo: Chinese-built F-6 (MiG-19SF)
Drawing: Mikoyan MiG-19PM

Data: MiG-19SF
Power plant: Two Klimov RD-9B turbojet engines (each 7 165 lb; 3 250 kg st with afterburning)
Wing span: 29 ft $6\frac{1}{4}$ in (9·00 m)
Length overall, excluding probe: 41 ft $1\frac{3}{4}$ in (12·54 m)
Max T-O weight: 19 180 lb (8 700 kg)
Max level speed at 32 800 ft (10 000 m): 783 knots (902 mph; 1 452 km/h)
Rate of climb at S/L: 22 638 ft (6 900 m)/min
Service ceiling: 58 725 ft (17 900 m)
Combat radius: 370 nm (425 miles; 685 km)
Armament: Three 30 mm NR-30 cannon. Underwing attachments for two air-to-air missiles, two rockets of up to 212 mm calibre, two packs of eight air-to-air rockets, two 250 kg bombs, drop-tanks or other stores
Ordered by: Air forces of Albania, Bulgaria, China, Cuba, Czechoslovakia, Egypt, Germany (Democratic Republic), Indonesia (Air Force and Navy), Iraq, Pakistan, Romania, USSR and Yugoslavia

MIKOYAN MiG-21 (USSR)

First flight 1955

NATO Code Name *Fishbed*
Single-seat day and all-weather fighter

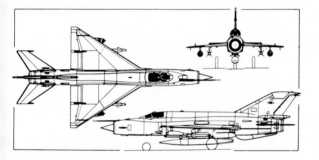

Data: MiG-21MF (Fishbed J)
Power plant: One Tumansky RD-11-300 turbojet engine (14 550 lb; 6 600 kg st with afterburning)
Wing span: 23 ft 5$\frac{1}{2}$ in (7·15 m)
Length, including pitot boom: 51 ft 8$\frac{1}{2}$ in (15·76 m)
Length, excluding pitot boom and intake centre-body: 44 ft 2 in (13·46 m)
T-O weight, with four K-13 missiles: 18 078 lb (8 200 kg)
Max level speed above 36 000 ft (11 000 m): 1 203 knots (1 385 mph; 2 230 km/h)
Service ceiling: 59 050 ft (18 000 m)
Range, internal fuel only: 593 nm (683 miles; 1 100 km)
Armament: Twin-barrel 23 mm cannon in lower fuselage. Four underwing pylons for weapons or drop-tanks, including two K-13 (Atoll) air-to-air missiles on inner pylons and UV-16-57 rocket packs, each with sixteen 57 mm rockets, on outer pylons.

Ordered by: Air forces of Afghanistan, Algeria, Bulgaria, China, Cuba, Czechoslovakia, Egypt, Finland, Germany (Democratic Republic), Hungary, India, Indonesia (Air Force and Navy), Iraq, North Korea, Poland, Romania, Somalia, South Yemen, Syria, USSR, North Vietnam and Yugoslavia

Drawing and Photo: MiG-21MF

MIKOYAN MiG-23 (USSR)

First flight about 1967

NATO Code Name *Flogger*
Single-seat supersonic fighter

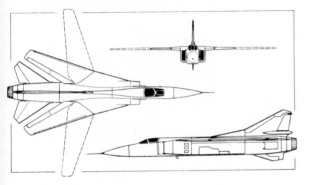

Data estimated
Power plant: One large afterburning turbojet engine
Wing span:
  fully spread: 50 ft 0 in (15·25 m)
  fully swept: 29 ft 6 in (9·00 m)
Length overall: 57 ft 0 in (17·40 m)
Normal T-O weight: 28 000 lb (12 700 kg)
Max level speed at height: with external stores
  1 233 knots (1 420 mph; 2 285 km/h)
Service ceiling: 50 000 ft (15 250 m)
Combat radius: 520 nm (600 miles; 960 km)
Ordered by: Soviet Air Force

MIKOYAN MiG-25 (USSR)

NATO Code Name *Foxbat*
Single-seat supersonic interceptor and reconnaissance-fighter

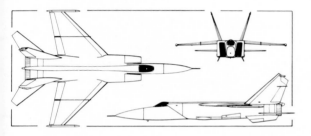

Data estimated
Power plant: Two turbojet engines (each 24 250 lb; 11 000 kg st with afterburning)
Wing span: 40 ft 0 in (12·20 m)
Length overall: 69 ft 0 in (21·00 m)
Max T-O weight: 64 200 lb (29 120 kg)
Max level speed at height: 1 836 knots (2 115 mph; 3 403 km/h)
Service ceiling: 73 000 ft (22 250 m)
Time to 36 000 ft (11 000 m), with afterburning: 2 min 30 sec
Normal combat radius: 610 nm (700 miles; 1 130 km)
Armament: Four underwing hard-points for air-to-air guided weapons. Internal weapons bay in fore-part of each air intake trunk
Ordered by: Soviet Air Force

MIL Mi-4 (USSR)

NATO Code Name *Hound*
Transport, anti-submarine and general utility helicopter

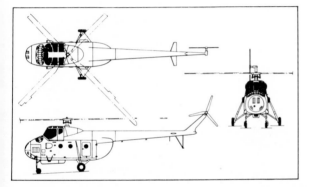

Photo: Mi-4 (ASW)

Power plant: One Shvetsov ASh-82V piston engine (1 700 hp)
Main rotor diameter: 68 ft 11 in (21·00 m)
Length of fuselage: 55 ft 1 in (16·80 m)
Max T-O weight: 17 200 lb (7 800 kg)
Max level speed at 4 920 ft (1 500 m): 113 knots (130 mph; 210 km/h)
Service ceiling: 18 000 ft (5 500 m)
Range with 8 passengers and 220 lb (100 kg) baggage: 217 nm (250 miles; 400 km)
Armament: Close-support version armed with a machine-gun in the front of the under-fuselage nacelle and air-to-surface rockets. The ASW version has a MAD towed 'bird' stowed against the rear of the fuselage pod, an under-nose search radar installation and flares, markers or sonobuoys mounted on the side of cabin forward of the main landing gear
Ordered by: Air forces of Afghanistan, Albania, Algeria, Bulgaria, China, Cuba, Czechoslovakia, Egypt, Finland, Germany (Democratic Republic), Hungary, India, Indonesia (Air Force and Army), Iraq, Khmer, North Korea, Mali, Mongolia, Poland, Romania, Sudan, Syria, USSR, North Vietnam, Yemen and Yugoslavia

MIL Mi-6 (USSR)

First flight 1957

NATO Code Name *Hook*
Heavy transport and assault helicopter

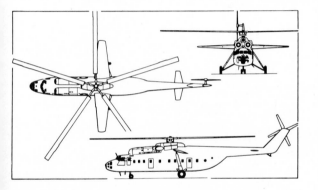

Power plant: Two Soloviev D-25V (TB-2BM) turbo-shaft engines (each 5 500 shp)
Main rotor diameter: 114 ft 10 in (35·00 m)
Length of fuselage: 108 ft 10½ in (33·18 m)
Max T-O weight for VTO: 93 700 lb (42 500 kg)
Max level speed: 162 knots (186 mph; 300 km/h)
Service ceiling: 14 750 ft (4 500 m)
Range with 13 228 lb (6 000 kg) payload: 350 nm (404 miles; 650 km)
Range with external tanks and 9 480 lb (4 300 kg) payload: 566 nm (652 miles; 1 050 km)
Max ferry range, tanks in cabin: 781 nm (900 miles; 1 450 km)
Armament and accommodation: A few are fitted with a gun of unknown calibre in the fuselage nose. Aircraft can accommodate a crew of 5 and either 65 passengers, 41 stretcher cases and two medical attendants, or military cargoes internally. Alternatively, a load of up to 19 840 lb (9 000 kg) can be carried on an external cargo sling
Ordered by: Air forces of Bulgaria, Egypt, Indonesia, USSR and North Vietnam

MIL Mi-8 (USSR)

NATO Code Name *Hip*
Medium transport and assault helicopter

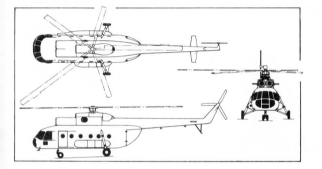

Power plant: Two Isotov TV2-117A turboshaft engines (each 1 700 shp)
Main rotor diameter: 69 ft $10\frac{1}{4}$ in (21·29 m)
Length of fuselage: 59 ft $7\frac{1}{4}$ in (18·17 m)
Max T-O weight for VTO: 26 455 lb (12 000 kg)
Max level speed:
  normal AUW: 135 knots (155 mph; 250 km/h)
  max AUW: 119 knots (137 mph; 220 km/h)
  with 5 510 lb (2 500 kg) of slung cargo: 97 knots (112 mph; 180 km/h)
Service ceiling: 14 750 ft (4 500 m)
Range:
  with 28 passengers and 30 min fuel reserves: 202 nm (233 miles; 375 km)
  with 8 820 lb (4 000 kg) cargo and 5% fuel reserves: 54 nm (62 miles; 100 km)
  with ferry tankage: 507 nm (584 miles; 940 km)
Armament and accommodation: Can be equipped with a twin rack for external stores, carried on out-rigger structure, on each side of the main cabin. Accommodation for up to 32 passengers or 12 stretchers and a medical attendant or internal/external freight
Ordered by: Air forces of Bulgaria, Czechoslovakia, Egypt, Ethiopia, Germany (Democratic Republic), Hungary, India, Iraq, Pakistan, Peru, Poland, Sudan, Syria and USSR

MYASISHCHEV Mya-4 (USSR)

NATO Code Name *Bison*
Long-range reconnaissance-bomber

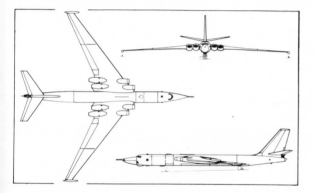

Data estimated
Power plant: Four Mikulin AM-3D turbojet engines
(each 19 180 lb; 8 700 kg st)
Wing span: 170 ft 0 in (51·82 m)
Length overall: 162 ft 0 in (49·37 m)
Max T-O weight: 350 000 lb (158 750 kg)
Max level speed at 36 000 ft (11 000 m): 486 knots
(560 mph; 901 km/h)
**Unrefuelled range with 10 000 lb (4 535 kg)
bombs:** at 452 knots (520 mph; 837 km/h):
6 080 nm (7 000 miles; 11 265 km)
Ordered by: Soviet Air Force

Photo and Drawing: Mya-4 (*Bison-C*)

NORTH AMERICAN F-86 SABRE (USA)

Single-seat tactical fighter and fighter-bomber

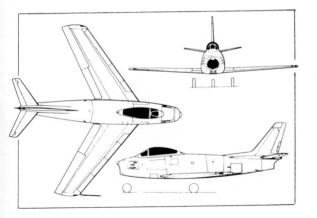

Data: F-86F Sabre
Power plant: One General Electric J47-GE-27 turbojet engine (5 970 lb; 2 708 kg st)
Wing span: 39 ft 1 in (11·91 m)
Length overall: 37 ft 6½ in (11·44 m)
Max T-O weight: 20 610 lb (9 350 kg)
Max level speed at S/L: 597 knots (687 mph; 1 105 km/h)
Range at 460 knots (530 mph; 853 km/h): 803 nm (925 miles; 1 485 km)
Armament: Six 0·50 in machine-guns in nose. Provision for two Sidewinder missiles, two 1 000 lb bombs or eight rockets under wings
Ordered by: Air forces of Argentine (28 F-86F), Burma (12 F-86F), Colombia (6 Canadair Sabre Mk 6 and some F-86F), Ethiopia (14 F-86F), Iran (90 ex-German Canadair Sabre Mk 6), Italy (63 F-86K), Japan (508 F-86F and 18 RF-86F), Jordan (4 F-86F), South Korea (40 F-86D, 122 F-86F and 10 RF-86F), Malaysia (10 Commonwealth CA-27 Sabre Mk 32), Pakistan (120 F-86F), Peru (14 F-86F), Philippines (18 F-86D and 40 F-86F), Portugal (50 F-86F), Saudi Arabia (11 F-86F), South Africa (34 Canadair Sabre Mk 6), Spain (244 F-86F), Taiwan (25 F-86D and 327 F-86F), Thailand (40 F-86F and approx 20 F-86L), USA (473 F-86H), Venezuela (22 F-86F) and Yugoslavia (130 F-86D/K, 10 RF-86F and 121 Canadair Sabre Mks 2/4)

Photo and Drawing: F-86F Sabre

NORTH AMERICAN F-100 SUPER SABRE (USA)

First flight 1953

Single-seat interceptor and fighter-bomber

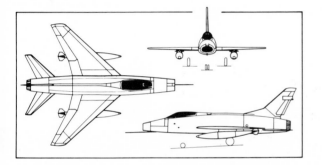

Photo and Drawing: F-100D Super Sabre

Data: F-100D Super Sabre

Power plant: One Pratt and Whitney J57-P-21A turbojet engine (17 000 lb; 7 710 kg st with afterburning)

Wing span: 38 ft 9 in (11·81 m)

Length overall: 54 ft 3 in (16·54 m)

Max T-O weight: 34 832 lb (15 800 kg)

Max level speed at 36 000 ft (11 000 m): 750 knots (864 mph; 1 390 km/h)

Range, with two external tanks: 1 300 nm (1 500 miles; 2 410 km)

Armament: Four 20 mm cannon in fuselage. Six underwing pylons for air-to-air or air-to-surface missiles, bombs, rockets etc

Ordered by: Air forces of Denmark (approx 50 F-100D and 8 F-100F), France (approx 75 F-100D and 7 F-100F), Taiwan (80 F-100A and some F-100F), Turkey (260 F-100C and some F-100F) and USA (203 F-100A/RF-100A, 476 F-100C, 1 274 F-100D and 339 F-100F)

NORTH AMERICAN T-28 TROJAN (USA)

First flight 1949

Tandem two-seat basic trainer and light ground attack aircraft

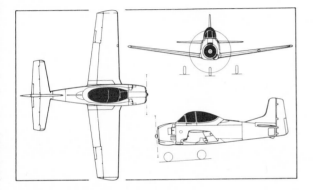

Photo: T-28D
Drawing: T-28C Trojan

Data: T-28D
Power plant: One Wright R-1820-56S piston engine (1 425 hp)
Wing span: 40 ft 7½ in (12·38 m)
Length overall: 32 ft 10 in (10·00 m)
Max T-O weight: 8 495 lb (3 853 kg)
Max level speed: 330 knots (380 mph; 610 km/h)
Range, with max weapon load: over 434 nm (500 miles; 804 km)
Armament: Two 0·50 in machine-gun packs, and provision for carrying bombs, rockets, napalm, etc, on six underwing racks
Ordered by: Air forces of Argentine (Air Force 34 T-28A, Navy approx 40 Sud-Aviation Fennec), Bolivia (2 T-28D), Brazil (18 T-28C), Ecuador (9 T-28A) ,Ethiopia (12 T-28A and 12 T-28D), Haiti (2 T-28A), Khmer (approx 4 T-28D), South Korea (T-28A/D), Laos (55 T-28D), Mexico (32 T-28A), Morocco (25 Fennec), Nicaragua (6 T-28), Philippines (12 T-28A), Taiwan (T-28D), Thailand (55 T-28D), Tunisia (Fennec), USA (Air Force 1 194 T-28A, of which 360 converted to T-28D; Navy 489 T-28B and 299 T-28C) and Zaïre (16 T-28D)

NORTH AMERICAN ROCKWELL RA-5C VIGILANTE (USA)

First flight 1958

Tandem two-seat carrier-borne reconnaissance aircraft

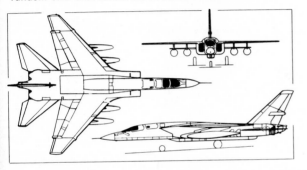

Power plant: Two General Electric J79-GE-10 turbo-jet engines (each 17 859 lb; 8 118 kg st with afterburning)
Wing span: 53 ft 0 in (16·15 m)
Length overall: 76 ft 7¼ in (23·35 m)
T-O weight, typical aircraft with fuel and reconnaissance equipment: 66 800 lb (30 300 kg)
Max level speed: 1 212 knots (1 385 mph; 2 228 km/h)
Service ceiling: 50 000 ft (15 240 m)
Range: 2 605 nm (3 000 miles; 4 830 km)
Armament: Variety of weapons, including thermo-nuclear bombs, can be accommodated on underwing attachments
Ordered by: US Navy (approx 160)

NORTHROP F-5 (USA)

First flight 1959

Lightweight tactical fighter and fighter-bomber

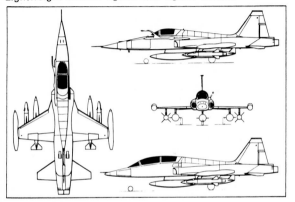

Photo: F-5A
Drawing: F-5A, with additional side view of F-5B
Data: F-5A
Power plant: Two General Electric J85-GE-13 turbojet engines (each 4 080 lb; 1 850 kg st with after burning)
Wing span: 25 ft 3 in (7·70 m)
Length overall: 47 ft 2 in (14·38 m)
Max T-O weight: 20 677 lb (9 379 kg)
Max level speed at 36 000 ft (11 000 m):
at AUW of 11 450 lb (5 193 kg): 803 knots (925 mph; 1 488 km/h)

Rate of climb at S/L, AUW as above: 28 700 ft (8 750 m)/min
Service ceiling, AUW as above: 50 500 ft (15 390 m)
Range with max fuel, with reserve fuel for 20 min max endurance at S/L, AUW as above, tanks retained: 1 205 nm (1 387 miles; 2 232 km)
Combat radius with max payload, AUW as above: allowances for 20 min max endurance at S/L and five min combat at S/L: 170 nm (195 miles; 314 km)
Armament: Interception weapons comprise two Sidewinder missiles on wingtip launchers and two 20 mm guns in fuselage nose. Five pylons, one under the fuselage and two under each wing, permit the carriage of a wide variety of other operational warloads. A bomb of more than 2 000 lb (910 kg) or high-rate-of-fire gun pack can be suspended from the centre pylon. Underwing loads can include four air-to-air missiles, Bullpup air-to-surface missiles, bombs, up to 20 air-to-surface rockets, gun packs or external fuel tanks. The reconnaissance nose does not eliminate the 20 mm nose gun capability
Ordered by: Air forces of Canada (89 CF-5A and 26 CF-5D), Ethiopia (12 F-5A and 2 F-5B), Greece (approx 75 F-5A and 4 or more F-5B), Iran (125 F-5A/B), South Korea (45 F-5A and 4 F-5B), Libya (7 F-5A and 2 F-5B), Morocco (12 F-5A and 4 F-5B), Netherlands (75 NF-5A and 30 NF-5D), Norway (68 F-5A, 32 RF-5A and 12 F-5B), Philippines (20 F-5A/B), Spain (36 SF-5A and 34 SF-5B), Taiwan (25 F-5A and small number of F-5B), Thailand (approx 25 F-5A and 2 F-5B), Turkey (140 F-5A and some F-5B) and South Vietnam (17 F-5A and 2 F-5B)

183

NORTHROP F-5E TIGER II (USA)

First flight 1972

Single-seat lightweight tactical fighter

Power plant: Two General Electric J85-GE-21 turbojet engines (each 5 000 lb; 2 267 kg st)
Wing span: 26 ft 8 in (8·13 m)
Length overall: 48 ft 3¾ in (14·73 m)

Max T-O weight: 21 820 lb (9 897 kg)
Max level speed at 36 000 ft (11 000 m):
  at AUW of 13 220 lb (5 997 kg): 917 knots (1 057 mph; 1 701 km/h)
Rate of climb at S/L, at above AUW: 31 600 ft (9 630 m)/min
Service ceiling, at above AUW: 54 000 ft (16 460 m)
Range with max fuel, with reserve fuel for 20 min max endurance at S/L, at above AUW, tanks retained: 1 715 nm (1 974 miles; 3175 km)
Combat radius at above AUW, with two Sidewinder missiles and max fuel:
  allowances as above and five minutes combat with max afterburning power at 15 000 ft (4 570 m): 760 nm (875 miles; 1 405 km)
Armament: Two AIM-9 Sidewinder missiles on wingtip launchers. Two M39A2 20 mm cannon mounted in fuselage nose. Up to 7 000 lb (3 175 kg) of mixed ordnance can be carried on the four underwing and one under-fuselage stations, including M129 leaflet bombs; MK-82 GP and Snakeye 500 lb bombs; MK-36 destructors; MK-83 1 000 lb bombs; MK-84 2 000 lb bombs; BLU-1, -27 or -32 U or F napalm; LAU-68 (7) 2·75 in rockets; LAU-3 (19) 2·75 in rockets; CBU-24, -49, -52 or -58; SUU-20 bomb and rocket packs; SUU-25 flare dispensers
Ordered by: Air Forces of Iran (141), Saudi Arabia, South Korea, South Vietnam, Taiwan and Thailand

NORTHROP YF-17 (USA)

Single-seat lightweight fighter

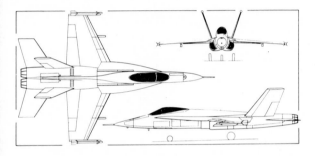

Power plant: Two General Electric YJ101 turbojet engines (each approx 15 000 lb; 6 804 kg st)
Wing span: 35 ft 0 in (10·67 m)
Length overall: 52 ft 0 in (15·85 m)
Max T-O weight: approx 19 600 lb (8 890 kg)
Armament: Two M39 20 mm guns and two infra-red missiles
Ordered by: US Air Force (2 prototypes for competitive evaluation in 1974 against General Dynamics YF-16)

PANAVIA MRCA (International)

Tandem two-seat multi-purpose combat aircraft

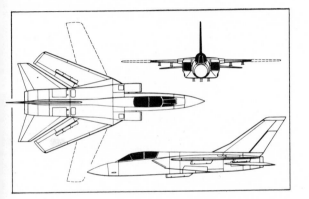

Power plant: Two Turbo-Union RB199-34R turbofan engines (each 14 500 lb; 6 577 kg st with afterburning)

Max T-O weight: approx 40 000 lb (18 140 kg)

Max level speed at high altitude: over 1 146 knots (1 320 mph; 2 124 km/h)

Armament: Ability to carry a wide variety of advanced non-nuclear weapons, including air-to-air and air-to-ground guided missiles, semi-active homing air-to-air weapons and conventional bombs

Ordered by: Governments of Federal Germany, Italy and UK (9 development aircraft, of which the first is due to fly in late 1973); orders anticipated for the air forces of Germany (approx 420), Italy (number unspecified) and UK (approx 350-400), subject to successful development programme

ROCKWELL B1 (USA)

Long-range supersonic strategic bomber

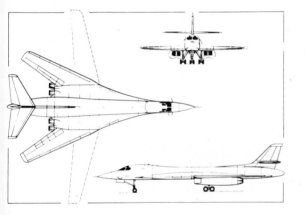

Power plant: Four General Electric F101 turbofan engines (each approx 30 000 lb; 13 600 kg st with afterburning)

Wing span:
fully spread: 137 ft 0 in (41·75 m)
fully swept: 78 ft 0 in (23·77 m)
Length overall: 143 ft 0 in (43·58 m)
Max T-O weight: 350 000-400 000 lb (158 750-181 450 kg)
Max level speed at 50 000 ft (15 240 m): approx 1 262 knots (1 454 mph; 2 340 km/h)
Max range without refuelling: 5 300 nm (6 100 miles; 9 800 km)
Armament: Among the penetration aids carried internally could be the Short Range Attack Missile (SRAM); the proposed Subsonic Cruise Armed Decoy (SCAD); the proposed Bomber Defence Missile (BDM); and nuclear and conventional weapons
Ordered by: US Air Force (3 flight development aircraft for evaluation from 1974; service requirement for about 250 aircraft, but no production order will be placed until after at least one year's flight test)

ROCKWELL OV-10 BRONCO (USA)

Tandem two-seat observation and counter-insurgency aircraft (OV-10A/B/C/E) and target tug (OV-10B(Z))

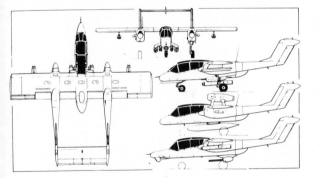

Photo: OV-10A Bronco
Drawing: OV-10A, with additional side views of OV-10B(Z) (centre) and YOV-10D (bottom)

Data: OV-10A Bronco
Power plant: Two AiResearch T76-G-410/411 turbo-prop engines (each 715 shp)
Wing span: 40 ft 0 in (12·19 m)
Length overall: 41 ft 7 in (12·67 m)
Overload T-O weight: 14 466 lb (6 563 kg)
Max level speed at S/L, without weapons: 244 knots (281 mph; 452 km/h)
Combat radius with max weapon load, no loiter: 198 nm (228 miles; 367 km)
Ferry range with auxiliary fuel: 1 240 nm (1 428 miles; 2 300 km)
Armament: Four weapon attachment points, each with capacity of 600 lb (272 kg), under short sponson extending from bottom of fuselage on each side, under wings. Fifth attachment point, capacity 1 200 lb (544 kg), under centre fuselage. Two 0·30 in M60C machine-guns carried in each sponson. Provision for carrying one Sidewinder missile on each wing. Max weapon load 3 600 lb (1 633 kg)
Ordered by: Air forces of Federal Germany (6 OV-10B and 12 OV-10B(Z)), Thailand (32 OV-10C), USA (Air Force, 157 OV-10A, Marine Corps, 114 OV-10A) and Venezuela (16 OV-10E)

SAAB 32 LANSEN (Sweden)

Single-seat attack (A 32A), fighter (J 32B) and photographic reconnaissance (S 32C) aircraft

Data: A 32A Lansen
Power plant: One Svenska Flygmotor RM5A2 (Rolls-Royce Avon) turbojet engine (9 920 lb; 4 500 kg st with afterburning)
Wing span: 42 ft $7\frac{3}{4}$ in (13·00 m)
Length overall: 48 ft $0\frac{3}{4}$ in (14·65 m)
Max T-O weight: 28 660 lb (13 000 kg)
Max level speed at S/L: 608 knots (700 mph; 1 125 km/h)
Rate of climb at S/L: 11 800 ft (3 600 m)/min
Service ceiling: 49 200 ft (15 000 m)
Max range: 1 735 nm (2 000 miles; 3 220 km)
Armament: Four 20 mm fuselage-mounted cannon. Underwing racks for two RB04 air-to-surface missiles, 24 rockets or bombs totalling 2 200 lb (1 000 kg)
Ordered by: Swedish Air Force (450 A 32A/J 32B/ S 32C, of which only the A 32A and S-32C remain in service)

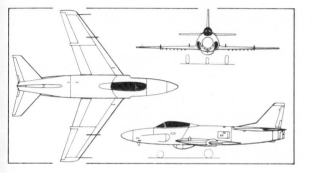

Photo and Drawing: A 32A Lansen

SAAB 35 DRAKEN (Sweden)

Single-seat fighter (J 35, F-35 and Saab 35S) and reconnaissance aircraft (S 35, RF-35) and tandem two-seat operational trainer (SK 35, TF-35)

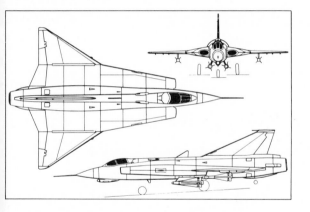

Photo: S 35E Draken
Drawing: J 35F Draken

Data: Saab 35S Draken
Power plant: One Volvo Flygmotor RM6C (Rolls-Royce Avon 300-series) turbojet engine (17 650 lb; 8 000 kg st with afterburning)

Wing span: 30 ft 10 in (9·40 m)
Length overall: 50 ft 4 in (15·35 m)
Max overload T-O weight: 35 275 lb (16 000 kg)
Max level speed with afterburning at 25 130 lb (11 400 kg) AUW: 1 146 knots (1 320 mph; 2 124 km/h)
Rate of climb at S/L with afterburning, above AUW: 34 450 ft (10 500 m)/min

Radius of action (high-low-high) internal fuel only: above AUW: 343 nm (395 miles; 635 km)
Radius of action (high-low-high) with two 1 000 lb bombs, two drop-tanks and AUW of 32 165 lb 14 590 kg): 541 nm (623 miles; 1 003 km)
Ferry range with max internal and external fuel: 1 754 nm (2 020 miles; 3 250 km)
Armament: Nine attachment points (each 1 000 lb; 454 kg) for external stores: three under each wing and three under fuselage. Stores can consist of air-to-air missiles and unguided air-to-air rocket pods (19 × 7·5 cm), 12 × 13·5 cm Bofors air-to-ground rockets, nine 1 000 lb or fourteen 500 lb bombs, or fuel tanks. Two or four RB24 Sidewinder air-to-air missiles can be carried under wings and fuselage. Two 30 mm Aden cannon (one in each wing) can be replaced by extra internal fuel tanks. With two 280 Imp gallon (1 275 litre) and two 110 Imp gallon (500 litre) drop-tanks, two 1 000 lb or four 500 lb bombs can be carried
Ordered by: Air forces of Denmark (20 F-35, 20 RF-35 and 6 TF-35), Finland (12 Saab 35S) and Sweden (more than 540 J 35/S 35/SK 35)

SAAB 37 VIGGEN (Sweden)

Single-seat attack/interceptor (AJ 37), photo-reconnaissance (SF 37) and sea surveillance aircraft (SH 37), and tandem two-seat operational trainer (SK 37); JA 37 interceptor/attack version under development

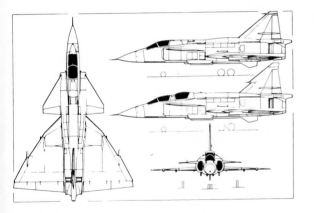

Data: AJ 37 Viggen

Power plant: One Volvo Flygmotor RM8 (supersonic development of the Pratt and Whitney JT8D-22) turbofan engine (26 000 lb; 11 800 kg st with afterburning)

Wing span: 34 ft 9¼ in (10·60 m)

Length overall (incl probe): 53 ft 5¾ in (16·30 m)

T-O weight with normal armament: approx 35 275 lb (16 000 kg)

Max level speed:
at high altitude: 1 146 knots (1 320 mph; 2 124 km/h)
at 330 ft (100 m): above 726 knots (836 mph; 1 345 km/h)

Time to 36 000 ft (11 000 m): approx 2 min

Tactical radius with external armament:
high-low-high: over 540 nm (620 miles; 1 000 km)
low altitude throughout: over 270 nm (310 miles; 500 km)

Armament: All armament is carried externally on seven permanent attachment points, three under fuselage and two under each wing. Wings can be fitted with two additional hard-points if required. Primary armament is the Swedish RB04 air-to-surface homing missile or the Saab RB05 air-to-surface missile, plus various types of air-to-surface rockets, bombs, 30 mm Aden guns and mines. The attack version can be adapted to perform interception missions armed with air-to-air missiles

Ordered by: Swedish Air Force (175 AJ 37/SF 37/ SH 37/SK 37)

Photo: AJ 37 Viggen
Drawing: AJ 37 Viggen, with additional side view of SK 37

SAAB 105 (Sweden)

Side-by-side two-seat basic trainer (SK 60) and light attack aircraft (Saab 105)

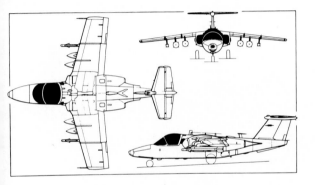

Data: Saab 105XT
Power plant: Two General Electric J85-GE-17B turbojet engines (each 2 850 lb; 1 293 kg st)
Wing span: 31 ft 2 in (9·50 m)
Length overall: 35 ft 5¼ in (10·80 m)
Max T-O weight, with armament: 14 330 lb (6 500 kg)
Max level speed at S/L:
at max T-O weight: 524 knots (603 mph; 970 km/h)
Range at 43 000 ft (13 100 m) at 378 knots (435 mph; 700 km/h): with external tanks and 30 min reserves: 1 580 nm (1 820 miles; 2 930 km)
Typical attack radius, including reserves, with 3 000 lb (1 360 kg) bomb load:
high-low-high mission: 420 nm (484 miles; 780 km)
low altitude throughout: 167 nm (192 miles; 310 km)
Armament: Three attachment points under each wing, the inner and outer points each capable of supporting a 610 lb (275 kg) load and the centre points each capable of supporting 1 000 lb (454 kg). Total weapons load 4 410 lb (2 000 kg), increased to 5 180 lb (2 350 kg) on Saab 105G. Wide range of weapons includes two 1 000 lb and four 500 lb bombs; four 500 lb bombs and two 30 mm gun pods; four 500 lb napalm bombs and two Minigun pods; twelve 13·5 cm rockets; six pods each containing four 5 in rockets; eighteen 7·5 cm rockets; two Saab RB05 air-to-surface and two infra-red (Sidewinder) air-to-air missiles and two Minigun pods
Ordered by: Air forces of Austria (40 Saab 105Ö) and Sweden (150 SK 60A/B/C)

Photo: Saab 105Ö
Drawing: Saab 105XT

SEPECAT JAGUAR (International)

Single-seat tactical support aircraft (Jaguar A and Jaguar GR Mk 1) and tandem two-seat advanced (Jaguar E) or operational trainer (Jaguar T Mk 2)

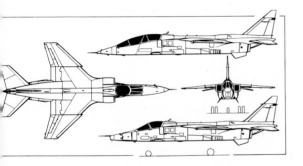

Photo: Jaguar GR Mk 1
Drawing: Jaguar GR Mk 1, with additional side view of Jaguar T Mk 2

Data: Jaguar A and GR Mk 1
Power plant: Two Rolls-Royce/Turboméca Adour turbofan engines (each 6 950 lb; 3 150 kg st with afterburning)
Wing span: 27 ft $10\frac{1}{4}$ in (8·49 m)
Length overall: 50 ft 11 in (15·52 m)
Max T-O weight: 32 600 lb (14 500 kg)
Max level speed:
at S/L: 729 knots (840 mph; 1 350 km/h)
at 36 000 ft (11 000 m): 860 knots (990 mph; 1 593 km/h)
Typical attack radius:
internal fuel only: 310-440 nm (357-507 miles; 575-815 km)
with external fuel: 450-710 nm (518-818 miles; 835-1 315 km)
Armament: Two 30 mm cannon in fuselage; 10 000 lb (4 500 kg) max external load of bombs, rockets, air-to-air missiles, photo-flares, camera pack or drop tanks on one under-fuselage attachment and four under wings; provision for wingtip air-to-air missiles
Ordered by: Air forces of France (59 Jaguar A and 40 Jaguar E) and UK (76 GR Mk 1 and 35 T Mk 2); planned procurement of approx 200 aircraft for each air force

SHIN MEIWA PS-1 (Japan)

STOL anti-submarine flying-boat (PS-1) and utility/search and rescue amphibian (US-1)

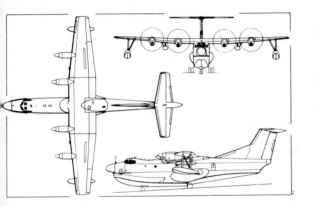

Photo and Drawing: PS-1

Data: PS-1

Power plant: Four Ishikawajima-built General Electric T64-IHI-10 turboprop engines (each 3 060 ehp)

Wing span: 108 ft 8¾ in (33·14 m)

Length overall: 109 ft 11 in (33·50 m)

Max T-O weight: 94 800 lb (43 000 kg)

Max level speed at 5 000 ft (1 525 m):
at normal T-O weight of 79 365 lb (36 000 kg):
295 knots (340 mph; 547 km/h)

Rate of climb at S/L: 2 264 ft (690 m)/min

Service ceiling: 29 500 ft (9 000 m)

Normal range: 1 169 nm (1 347 miles; 2 168 km)

Armament and equipment: No built-in armament. Two homing torpedoes in a pod under each wing, between engines; launcher under each wingtip for three 5 in air-to-surface rockets; dipping sonar; acoustic search and echo ranging gear in hull, with 20 sonobuoys, 30 explosive charges, four 330 lb bombs and smoke bombs; search radar in nose, MAD in retractable tailboom, searchlight under starboard wing

Ordered by: Japan (Navy 23 PS-1 and 3 US-1)

SIKORSKY S-58/H-34 SEABAT, SEAHORSE and CHOCTAW (USA) and WESTLAND WESSEX (UK)

General-purpose and anti-submarine helicopter
Data: SH-34G

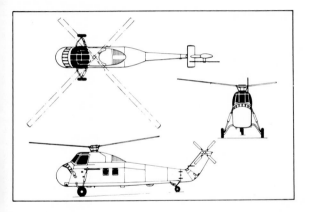

Power plant: One Wright R-1820-84B/D piston engine (1 525 hp)
Main rotor diameter: 56 ft 0 in (17·07 m)

Length overall: 56 ft 8¼ in (17·27 m)
Max permissible weight: 14 000 lb (6 350 kg)
Max level speed at S/L at 13 000 lb (5 900 kg) AUW: 106 knots (122 mph; 196 km/h)
Max rate of climb at S/L at above AUW: 1 100 ft (335 m)/min
Service ceiling at above AUW: 9 500 ft (2 900 m)
Range with max fuel, 10% reserve: at above AUW: 214 nm (247 miles; 400 km)
Armament and accommodation: Cabin for up to 18 troops or eight stretchers. SH-34 anti-submarine helicopter can carry weapons
Ordered by:
US MODELS: Air forces of Belgium (7 S-58/H-34), Brazil (Navy 5 SH-34J), France (Air Force/Navy 166 CH-34A/SH-34G/J), German Federal Republic (Navy 25 SH-34G, Army approx 90 CH-34A), Italy (Navy 9 SH-34J), Japan (Navy 14 HSS-1), Khmer (3 H-34), Laos (4 HUS-1), Netherlands (Navy 6 UH-34J), Philippines (2 H-34), Taiwan (Army 7 H-34), Thailand (20 CH-34C), USA (Navy/Marine Corps more than 500 UH-34D/VH-34D/LH-34D, UH-34E, SH-34G/H/J and UH-34G/J, Coast Guard 6 HH-34F, Army 437 CH-34A/B/C), South Vietnam (approx 40 CH-34) and Uruguay (Navy 1 SH-34)
WESSEX: Air forces of Australia (Navy 27 HAS Mk 31), Bangla Desh (2), Brunei (1 Mk 54), Ghana (3 Mk 53), Iraq (12 Mk 52) and UK (Air Force approx 60 HC Mk 2 and 2 HCC Mk 4; Navy approx 150 HAS Mk 1/HAS Mk 3/HU Mk 5)

SIKORSKY S-61A/B and H-3 SEA KING (USA)

Anti-submarine, search and rescue and transport helicopter

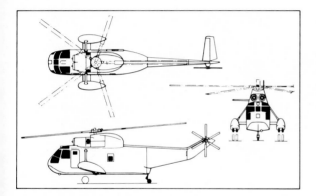

Photo: Agusta-built Sikorsky SH-3D Sea King
Drawing: Sikorsky SH-3D Sea King

Data: Sikorsky SH-3D Sea King
Power plant: Two General Electric T58-GE-10 turbo-shaft engines (each 1 400 shp)
Main rotor diameter: 62 ft 0 in (18·90 m)
Length overall: 72 ft 8 in (22·15 m)
Normal T-O weight: 18 626 lb (8 450 kg)
Max level speed, at 20 500 lb (9 300 kg) AUW: 144 knots (166 mph; 267 km/h)
Max rate of climb at S/L, at above AUW: 2 200 ft (670 m)/min
Service ceiling, at above AUW: 14 700 ft (4 480 m)
Range with max fuel, 10% reserve at above AUW: 542 nm (625 miles; 1 005 km)
Armament: Provision for 840 lb (381 kg) of weapons, including homing torpedoes
Ordered by: Air forces of Argentine (Navy 4 S-61D-4), Brazil (Navy 4 SH-3D), Canada (41 CHSS-2), Denmark (9 S-61A), Indonesia (1 S-61A), Iran (Navy 10 Agusta-Sikorsky SH-3D), Italy (Navy more than 24 Agusta-Sikorsky SH-3D), Japan (Navy 54 SH-3A/D and 2 S-61), Malaysia (16 S-61A-4 Nuri), Spain (Navy 6 Agusta-Sikorsky SH-3D) and USA (Air Force 3 CH-3B; Navy approx 300 SH-3A/D, 9 RH-3A, HH-3A, approx 25 SH-3G and 11 SH-3H; Marine Corps 6 VH-3A; Army 2 VH-3A)

SIKORSKY S-61R/H-3C/E (USA)

Troop transport, assault and rescue helicopter

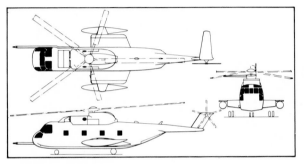

Photo: HH-3E
Drawing: CH-3E

Data: CH-3E
Power plant: Two General Electric T58-GE-5 turbo-shaft engines (each 1 500 shp)
Main rotor diameter: 62 ft 0 in (18·90 m)
Length overall: 73 ft 0 in (22·25 m)
Normal T-O weight: 21 247 lb (9 635 kg)
Max level speed at S/L: 141 knots (162 mph; 261 km/h)
Max rate of climb at S/L: 1 310 ft (400 m)/min
Service ceiling: 11 100 ft (3 385 m)
Range with max fuel, 10% reserve: 404 nm (465 miles; 748 km)
Armament: Pod-mounted turret armament system located off each sponson, mounting an Emerson Electric TAT-102 turret, incorporating a General Electric six-barrel 7·62 mm Minigun
Ordered by: United States Air Force (133 CH-3C/CH-3E/HH-3E) and Coast Guard (34 HH-3F Pelican)

SIKORSKY S-64 SKYCRANE/CH-54 TARHE (USA)

First flight 1962

Heavy-lift helicopter

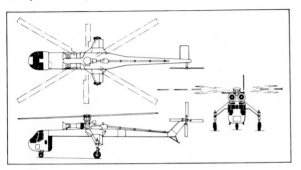

Photo: CH-54B Tarhe
Drawing: CH-54A

Data: CH-54A
Power plant: Two Pratt and Whitney T73-P-1 turboshaft engines (each 4 500 shp max rating)
Main rotor diameter: 72 ft 0 in (21·95 m)
Length overall: 88 ft 6 in (26·97 m)
Max T-O weight: 42 000 lb (19 050 kg)
Max level speed at S/L:
  at normal T-O weight of 38 000 lb (17 237 kg):
  110 knots (127 mph; 204 km/h)
Max rate of climb at S/L:
  at normal T-O weight: 1 700 ft (518 m)/min
Service ceiling:
  at normal T-O weight: 13 000 ft (3 960 m)
Range with max fuel, 10% reserve:
  at normal T-O weight: 219 nm (253 miles; 407 km)
Accomodation: With a max loaded weight of 20 000 lb (9 072 kg), each detachable under-fuselage pod accommodates 45 combat-equipped troops, or 24 litters, or cargo
Ordered by: US Army (80 CH-54A/B)

SIKORSKY S-65/H-53 SEA STALLION (USA)

Heavy assault transport helicopter

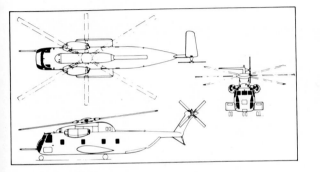

Photo: CH-53G, built in Germany
Drawing: CH-53D Sea Stallion

Data: CH-53D Sea Stallion
Power plant: Two General Electric T64-GE-412 or T64-GE-413 turboshaft engines (each -412 having a military rating of 3 695 shp and each -413 a max rating of 3 925 shp)
Main rotor diameter: 72 ft 3 in (22·02 m)
Length overall, rotors turning: 88 ft 3 in (26·90 m)
Max T-O weight: 42 000 lb (19 050 kg)
Max level speed at S/L: 170 knots (196 mph; 315 km/h)
Max rate of climb at S/L: 2 180 ft (664 m)/min
Service ceiling: 21 000 ft (6 400 m)
Range, with 4 076 lb (1 849 kg) fuel:
10% reserve at cruising speed and 2 min warm-up: 223 nm (257 miles; 413 km)
Accommodation: 38 combat-equipped troops or 24 stretchers and four attendants, or cargo
Ordered by: Air forces of Austria (2 S-65-Oe), German Federal Republic (153 CH-53G), Israel (10 CH-53) and USA (Air Force 66 HH-53B/C; Navy 39 RH-53D; Marine Corps approx 265 CH-53A/D)

SOKO J-1 JASTREB (Yugoslavia)

First flight 1967

Single-seat light attack aircraft

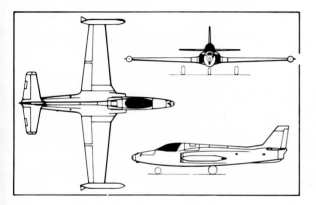

Power plant: One Rolls-Royce Bristol Viper 531 turbojet engine (3 000 lb; 1 360 kg st)
Wing span: 34 ft 8 in (10·56 m)
Length overall: 35 ft 1½ in (10·71 m)
Max T-O weight: 10 287 lb (4 666 kg)
Max level speed at 19 680 ft (6 000 m), at AUW of 8 748 lb (3 968 kg): 442 knots (510 mph; 820 km/h)
Rate of climb at S/L, at above AUW: 4 135 ft (1 260 m)/min
Service ceiling, at above AUW: 39 375 ft (12 000 m)

Max range at 29 520 ft (9 000 m):
with tip tanks full: 820 nm (945 miles; 1 520 km)
Armament: Three 0·50 in Colt-Browning machine-guns in nose. Total of eight underwing weapon attachments. Two inboard attachments can carry two bombs of up to 550 lb (250 kg) each, two clusters of small bombs, two 150 litre napalm tanks, two pods each with 12 × 57 mm rockets, or two 100 lb (45 kg) photo flares. Other attachments can each carry a 127 mm rocket
Ordered by: Air forces of Yugoslavia (30) and Zambia (4)

SOKO P-2 KRAGUJ (Yugoslavia)

Single-seat lightweight close-support aircraft

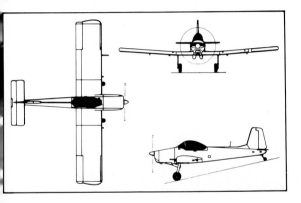

Power plant: One Lycoming GSO-480-B1A6 piston engine (340 hp)
Wing span: 34 ft 11 in (10·64 m)
Length overall: 26 ft 0¼ in (7·93 m)
Max T-O weight: 3 580 lb (1 624 kg)
Max level speed at S/L: 148 knots (171 mph; 275 km/h)
Max level speed at 5 000 ft (1 500 m): 159 knots (183 mph; 295 km/h)
Rate of climb at S/L, at AUW of 2 857 lb (1 296 kg): 1 575 ft (480 m)/min
Range with max fuel: 431 nm (500 miles; 800 km)
Armament: One 7·7 mm machine-gun in each wing. Total of six underwing weapon attachments. Two inner attachments each carry a bomb of up to 100 kg, cluster of small bombs, 150 litre napalm tank or 12-round rocket pack. Other four attachments each carry a 57 mm or 127 mm rocket
Ordered by: Yugoslav Air Force (30)

SUD-AVIATION VAUTOUR (France)

Single-seat ground attack aircraft (IIA), tandem two-seat light bomber (IIB) or two-seat all-weather fighter (IIN)

Data: SO 4050 Vautour IIN
Power plant: Two SNECMA Atar 101E-3 turbojet engines (each 7 720 lb; 3 500 kg st)
Wing span: 49 ft 6½ in (15·09 m)
Length overall: 51 ft 1 in (15·57 m)
Max T-O weight: 45 635 lb (20 700 kg)
Max level speed at S/L: 595 knots (686 mph; 1 100 km/h)
Range: 2 155 nm (2 485 miles; 4 000 km)
Armament: Four 30 mm DEFA cannon. 232 rockets in two packs in fuselage and underwing attachments for four Matra R 511 air-to-air missiles
Ordered by: Air forces of France (40 IIB and 70 IIN) and Israel (25 IIA)

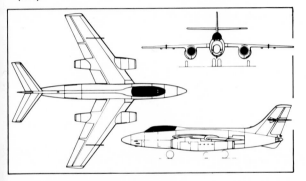

Photo: SO 4050 Vautour IIA
Drawing: SO 4050 Vautour IIN

SUKHOI Su-7B (USSR)

NATO Code Name *Fitter-A*
Single-seat ground attack fighter

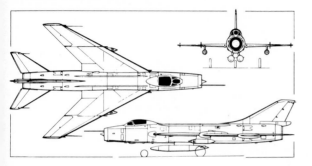

Power plant: One Lyulka AL-7F (Soviet designation TRD31) turbojet engine (22 046 lb; 10 000 kg st with afterburning)
Wing span: 29 ft $3\frac{1}{2}$ in (8·93 m)
Length overall, including probe: 57 ft 0 in (17·37 m)
Max T-O weight: 29 750 lb (13 500 kg)
Max level speed at 36 000 ft (11 000 m):
  clean: 917 knots (1 055 mph; 1 700 km/h)
Rate of climb at S/L: approx 29 900 ft (9 120 m)/min
Service ceiling: 49 700 ft (15 150 m)
Combat radius: 172-260 nm (200-300 miles; 320-480 km)
Max range: 780 nm (900 miles; 1 450 km)
Armament: Attachments for external stores, including rocket packs and bombs (usually two 1 650 lb; 750 kg and two 1 100 lb; 500 kg), under each wing. A pair of external fuel tanks can be carried under the centre fuselage, but these reduce the max external weapon load to 2 200 lb (1 000 kg). A 30 mm NR-30 cannon is installed in each wing-root leading-edge
Ordered by: Air forces of Cuba, Czechoslovakia, Egypt, Germany (Democratic Republic), Hungary, India, Poland, USSR and North Vietnam

SUKHOI Su-7, VARIABLE-GEOMETRY VERSION (USSR)

First flight about 1967

NATO Code Name *Fitter-B*
Single 1-1 seat tactical fighter

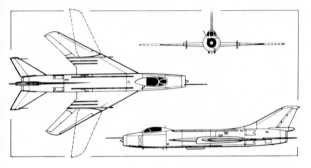

Power plant: One Lyulka AL-7F (TRD 31) turbojet
engine (22 046 lb; 10 000 kg st with afterburning)
Wing span (estimated):
  spread: 41 ft 0 in (12·50 m)
  swept: 29 ft 6 in (9·00 m)
Length overall, including probe (estimated):
  56 ft 0 in (17·00 m).
Other details basically similar to those of *'Fitter-A'*
Ordered by: Soviet Air Force

SUKHOI Su-9 (USSR)

NATO Code Name *Fishpot*
Single-seat all-weather fighter

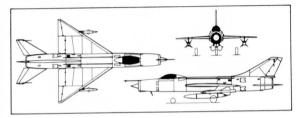

Power plant: One Lyulka AL-7F (TRD31) turbojet
engine (22 046 lb; 10 000 kg st with afterburning)
Wing span (estimated): 26 ft 0 in (7·90 m)
Length overall, including probe (estimated):
56 ft 0 in (17·00 m)
**Max level speed at 36 000 ft (11 000 m) (est-
imated):** 1 033 knots (1 190 mph; 1 915 km/h)
Armament: Two 'Anab' missiles under wings, one
with radar homing head and one with infra-red
homing head
Ordered by: Soviet Air Force

SUKHOI Su-11 (USSR)

NATO Code Name *Flagon-A*
Single-seat supersonic interceptor

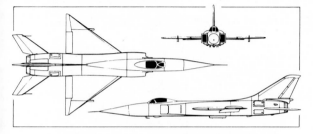

Photo and Drawing: Su-11 (*Flagon-A*)

First flight about 1966

Data estimated

Power plant: Two afterburning turbojets, with variable-area nozzles, mounted side by side in rear fuselage

Wing span: 30 ft 0 in (9·15 m)

Length overall: 68 ft 0 in (20·50 m)

Max T-O weight: 35 275 lb (16 000 kg)

Max level speed above 36 000 ft (11 000 m): 1 320 knots (1 520 mph; 2 445 km/h)

Armament: Single pylon for external store under each wing. Normal armament comprises one radar homing and one infra-red homing 'Anab' air-to-air missile. Side-by-side pylons under centre fuselage for further weapons or external fuel tanks

Ordered by: Soviet Air Force

TUPOLEV VARIABLE-GEOMETRY BOMBER (USSR)

NATO Code Name *Backfire*
Three-seat long-range supersonic bomber

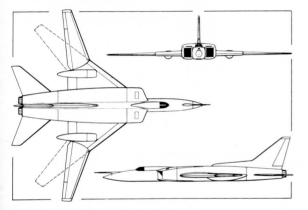

Power plant: Two turbofan engines (possibly Kuznetsov NK-144s, each 38 580 lb; 17 500 kg st with afterburning)

Loaded weight: approx 272 000 lb (123 350 kg)

Design over-target speed: approx 1 300-1 430 knots (1 500-1 650 mph; 2 415-2 655 km/h)

Range, unrefuelled: up to 4 000 nm (4 600 miles; 7 400 km)

Armament: Full range of Soviet free-fall weapons and an air-to-surface stand-off missile at least as advanced as 'Kitchen'. Developments like the US SRAM and decoy missile range may be carried

Ordered by: Under development for Soviet Air Force. Two prototypes and about 10 pre-production aircraft reported to have flown by late 1972

Photo: Model of *Backfire* (provisional)

TUPOLEV Tu-16 (USSR)

First flight about 1954

NATO Code Name *Badger*
Medium bomber, reconnaissance-bomber and ECM
aircraft

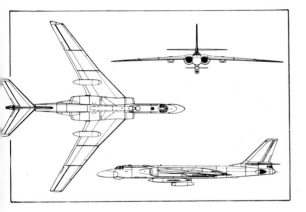

Power plant: Two Mikulin AM-3M turbojet engines
(each 20 950 lb; 9 500 kg st)
Wing span: 110 ft 0 in (33·50 m)
Length overall: 120 ft 0 in (36·50 m)
Normal T-O weight: approx 150 000 lb (68 000 kg)
Max level speed at 35 000 ft (10 700 m):
at max T-O weight, estimated: 510 knots (587 mph;
945 km/h)
Service ceiling: 42 650 ft (13 000 m)
Range with max bomb load: 2 605 nm (3 000 miles;
4 800 km)
Range at 417 knots (480 mph; 770 km/h):
with 6 600 lb (3 000 kg) of bombs: 3 450 nm
(3 975 miles; 6 400 km)
Armament: Forward dorsal and rear ventral barbettes
each containing two 23 mm cannon. Two further
cannon in tail position controlled by an automatic
gun-ranging radar set. Seventh, fixed cannon on
starboard side of nose of versions without nose
radome. Bomb load of up to 19 800 lb (9 000 kg)
in internal weapons bay. Naval versions can carry
air-to-surface winged stand-off missiles under wings
Ordered by: Air forces of Egypt, Indonesia (Air Force
and Navy), Iraq and USSR (Air Force and Navy)

Photo: Tu-16 (*Badger-D*)
Drawing: Tu-16 (*Badger-C*) with *Kipper* missile

233

TUPOLEV Tu-22 (USSR)

NATO Code Name *Blinder*
Three-seat supersonic bomber

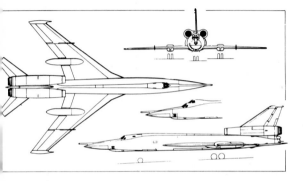

Data estimated
Power plant: Two turbojet engines (each 26 000 lb;
11 800 kg st with afterburning)
Wing span: 90 ft 10½ in (27·70 m)
Length overall: 132 ft 11½ in (40·53 m)
Max T-O weight: 184 970 lb (83 900 kg)
Max level speed at 40 000 ft (12 200 m): 800 knots
(920 mph; 1 480 km/h)
Service ceiling: 60 000 ft (18 300 m)
Max range: 1 215 nm (1 400 miles; 2 250 km)
Armament: *Blinder-A* has fuselage weapon bay for
free-fall bombs. *Blinder-B* is equipped to carry the
'Kitchen' air-to-surface missile and has a larger
radome in nose. A version of this aircraft equipped for
electronic countermeasures (ECM) duties has been
reported in service
Ordered by: Soviet Air Force

Photo: Tu-22 (*Blinder-B*)
Drawing: Tu-22 (*Blinder-A*), with scrap view of
training version

TUPOLEV Tu-28P (USSR)

First flight about 1961

NATO Code Name *Fiddler*
Two-seat all-weather fighter

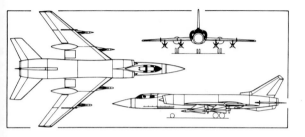

Data estimated
Power plant: Two afterburning turbojet engines
Wing span: 65 ft 0 in (20·00 m)
Length overall: 98 ft 6 in (30·00 m)
Max T-O weight: 100 000 lb (45 000 kg)
Max level speed: 1 000 knots (1 150 mph; 1 850 km/h)
Armament: Two 'Ash' missiles under each wing, one usually of the radar homing type and the other of the infra-red homing type
Ordered by: Soviet Air Force

TUPOLEV Tu-95 (USSR)

NATO Code Name *Bear*
Long-range bomber and maritime reconnaissance aircraft

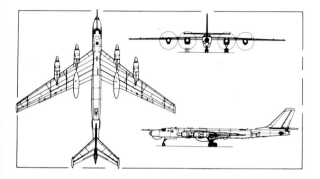

Data: Tu-95 (*Bear-A*)
Power plant: Four Kuznetsov NK-12M turboprop engines (each 14 795 ehp)
Wing span: approx 159 ft 0 in (48·50 m)
Length overall: approx 155 ft 10 in (47·50 m)
Max T-O weight: approx 340 000 lb (154 220 kg)
Max level speed at 41 000 ft (12 500 m): approx 434 knots (500 mph; 805 km/h)
Range: approx 6 775 nm (7 800 miles; 12 555 km)
Armament: Three pairs of 23 mm cannon in remotely-controlled dorsal and ventral barbettes and tail position, and (*Bear-A* only) one on starboard side of nose. Up to 25 000 lb (11 340 kg) of bombs in internal bay, or (*Bear-B*) one *Kangaroo* long-range jet-powered air-to-surface missile under fuselage
Ordered by: Soviet Air Force

Photo and Drawing: Tu-95 (*Bear-D*)

TUPOLEV Tu-114, EARLY WARNING AND FIGHTER CONTROL VERSION (USSR)

First flight about 1967

NATO Code Name *Moss*
Airborne warning and control post aircraft

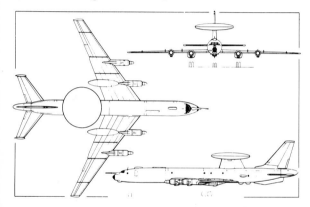

Power plant: Four Kuznetsov NK-12MV turboprop engines (each 14 795 ehp)
Wing span: approx 168 ft 0 in (51·20 m)
Length overall: approx 188 ft 0 in (57·30 m)
Normal T-O weight: approx 360 000 lb (163 295 kg)
Max continuous cruising speed at 25 000 ft (7 620 m): approx 400 knots (460 mph; 740 km/h)
Service ceiling: approx 39 000 ft (11 885 m)
Range, unrefuelled: more than 3 475 nm (4 000 miles; 6 435 km)
Ordered by: Soviet Air Force

VOUGHT A-7 CORSAIR II (USA)

Single-seat carrier- and land-based attack aircraft

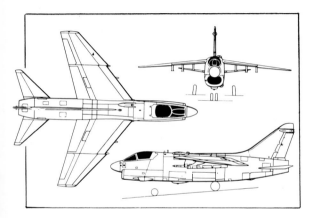

Data: A-7D Corsair II
Power plant: One Allison non-afterburning TF41-A-1 (Rolls-Royce Spey 168-62) turbofan engine (14 250 lb; 6 465 kg st)
Wing span: 38 ft 9 in (11·80 m)
Length overall: 46 ft 1½ in (14·06 m)
Max T-O weight: 42 000 lb (19 050 kg)
Max level speed at S/L: 606 knots (698 mph; 1 123 km/h)
Max ferry range: more than 2 900 nm (3 340 miles; 5 375 km)
Armament: One forward firing M61-A1 Vulcan 20 mm multi-barrel cannon in fuselage; two stations under fuselage and six under wings for more than 15 000 lb (6 805 kg) of external stores including air-to-air missiles, air-to-surface missiles, bombs, rockets, gun pods and drop-tanks
Ordered by: United States Air Force (387 A-7D) and Navy (199 A-7A, 196 A-7B, 67 A-7C and 427 A-7E)

Photo and Drawing: A-7D Corsair II

VOUGHT F-8 CRUSADER (USA)

Single-seat carrier-based day fighter (F-8) and reconnaissance aircraft (RF-8)

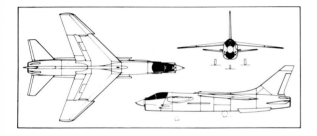

Photo: F-8E(FN) Crusader
Drawing: F-8E Crusader

Data: F-8E Crusader
Power plant: One Pratt and Whitney J57-P-20 turbojet engine (18 000 lb; 8 165 kg st with afterburning)
Wing span: 35 ft 8 in (10·87 m)
Length overall: 54 ft 6 in (16·61 m)
Max T-O weight: 34 000 lb (15 420 kg)
Max level speed: nearly 1 148 knots (1 322 mph; 2 127 km/h)
Armament: Four 20 mm Colt cannon in fuselage nose. Four Sidewinder missiles mounted externally on sides of fuselage. Late-production F-8Es have two underwing pylons for attack weapons including two 1 000 lb or 2 000 lb bombs, four 500 lb bombs, twelve 250 lb bombs or 24 Zuni rockets. Eight more Zunis can replace the four fuselage-mounted Sidewinders. French Navy F-8E(FN) has provision to carry Matra R 530 air-to-air missiles in addition to Sidewinders
Ordered by: Navies of France (42 F-8E(FN)) and USA (318 F-8A/TF-8A, 144 RF-8A of which 53 converted to RF-8G, 130 F-8B of which 63 converted to F-8L, 187 F-8C of which 87 converted to F-8K, 152 F-8D of which 89 converted to F-8H, and 286 F-8E of which 136 converted to F-8J)

WESTLAND/AÉROSPATIALE LYNX (UK/France)

General-purpose and anti-submarine helicopter

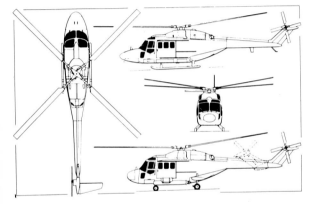

Photo: Lynx HAS Mk 2
Drawing: Lynx AH Mk 1, with additional side view of Lynx HAS Mk 2

Data: Lynx HAS Mk 2
Power plant: Two Rolls-Royce BS 360-07-26 turboshaft engines (each 900 shp max contingency rating)
Main rotor diameter: 42 ft 0 in (12·80 m)
Length overall, rotors turning: 49 ft 9 in (15·16 m)
Design max T-O weight: 9 250 lb (4 196 kg)
Max never-exceed speed at 8 000 lb (3 628 kg) AUW: 180 knots (207 mph; 333 km/h)

Typical radius at S/L:
with crew of two and 5% reserves, no loiter: 156 nm (179 miles; 289 km)
with crew of two and 5% reserves, 60 min loiter: 88 nm (101 miles; 163 km)

Armament: Two Mk 44 homing torpedoes or alternative weapons, mounted externally one each side of the cabin. BAC CL834 homing missiles for attacking light surface craft; alternatively AS 12 or similar wire-guided missiles can be employed
Ordered by: Argentine Navy (2 of anti-submarine version) and UK/French governments (12 development aircraft). Production aircraft to be ordered for French Navy (80), British Army (approx 150 AH Mk 1) and Royal Navy (approx 100 HAS Mk 2) initially

WESTLAND SEA KING (UK)

Multi-purpose helicopter

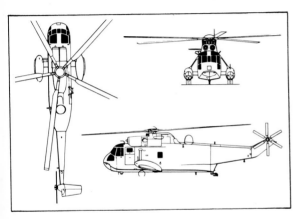

Data: Sea King HAS Mk 1

Power plant: Two Rolls-Royce Bristol Gnome H 1400 turboshaft engines (each 1 500 shp)

Main rotor diameter: 62 ft 0 in (18·90 m)

Length overall, rotors turning: 72 ft 8 in (22.15 m)

Max T-O weight: 20 500 lb (9 300 kg)

Normal operating speed: 114 knots (131 mph; 211 km/h)

Max rate of climb at S/L: 1 770 ft (540 m)/min

Approved ceiling: 10 000 ft (3 050 m)

Ferry/transit range (SAR version): Standard fuel: 520 nm (598 miles; 963 km)

Operational equipment, ASW model: Plessey Type 195 dipping sonar, AD 580 Doppler navigation system, AW 391 search radar in dorsal radome, transponder beneath rear fuselage, two No 4 marine markers, four No 2 Mk 2 smoke floats, up to four Mk 44 homing torpedoes, four Mk 11 depth charges, one Clevite simulator or air-to-surface missiles. For secondary rôle a mounting is provided on the aft frame of the starboard door for a machine-gun

Ordered by: Air force of Norway (10 Mk 43), and Navies of Australia (10 Mk 50), German Federal Republic (22 Mk 41), India (9 Mk 42), Pakistan (4 or 6) and UK (56 HAS Mk 1)

WESTLAND SCOUT and WASP (UK)

Light liaison (Scout) or anti-submarine helicopter (Wasp)

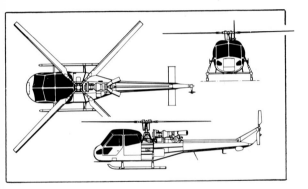

Photo: Wasp HAS Mk 1
Drawing: Scout AH Mk 1

Data: Wasp HAS Mk 1
Power plant: One Rolls-Royce Bristol Nimbus 503 turboshaft engine (derated to 710 shp)
Main rotor diameter: 32 ft 3 in (9·83 m)
Length overall, rotors turning: 40 ft 4 in (12·29 m)
Max T-O weight: 5 500 lb (2 495 kg)
Max level speed at S/L: 104 knots (120 mph; 193 km/h)
Max rate of climb at S/L: 1 440 ft (439 m)/min
Max range with standard fuel: 263 nm (303 miles; 488 km)
Range with max fuel:
    including allowances of 5 min for T-O and landing, and 15 min cruising at best cruising height, with 4 passengers: 234 nm (270 miles; 435 km)
Armament: Two Mk 44 homing torpedoes or other stores carried externally
Ordered by:
    SCOUT: Royal Australian Navy (2), Bahrain Police (2), British Army (approx 150 AH Mk 1) and Uganda Police Air Wing (2)
    WASP: Navies of Brazil (3), the Netherlands (12), New Zealand (3), South Africa (17) and UK (approx 80 HAS Mk 1)

YAKOVLEV Yak-25, Yak-26 and Yak-27 (USSR)   First flights about 1953/1956/1956

NATO Code Names *Flashlight* and *Mangrove*
Two-seat all-weather fighter (Yak-25 *Flashlight-A* and Yak-27 *Flashlight-C*), ground attack (Yak-25R *Flashlight-B*) and tactical reconnaissance aircraft (Yak-26 *Mangrove*)

Data: Yak-26 (estimated)
Power plant: Two Klimov RD-9 turbojet engines (each 8 820 lb; 4 000 kg st with afterburning)
Wing span: 38 ft 6 in (11·75 m)
Length overall, including nose-probe: 62 ft 0 in (18·90 m)
Normal T-O weight: 25 000 lb (11 350 kg)
Max level speed at 36 000 ft (11 000 m): 544 knots (627 mph; 1 009 km/h)
Armament: Single 30 mm gun in fairing under starboard side of front fuselage
Ordered by: Soviet Air Force

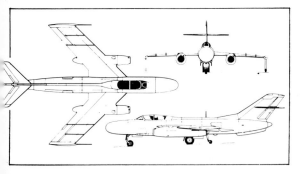

Photo: Yak-26
Drawing: Yak-25

YAKOVLEV Yak-28 and Yak-28P (USSR)

NATO Code Names *Firebar* and *Brewer*
Two-seat multi-purpose tactical aircraft (Yak-28
Brewer) and all-weather fighter (Yak-28P *Firebar*)

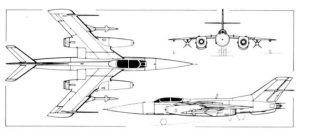

Photo and Drawing: Yak-28P

Data: Yak-28P (estimated)
Power plant: Two turbojet engines, believed to be
of same basic type as Tumansky RD-11 (each 13 120
lb; 5 950 kg st with afterburning)
Wing span: 42 ft 6 in (12·95 m)
Length overall: 71 ft 0½ in (21·65 m)
Max T-O weight: 35 000 lb (15 875 kg)
Max level speed at 35 000 ft (10 670 m): 636
knots (733 mph; 1 180 km/h)
Service ceiling: 55 000 ft (16 750 m)
Max range: 1 040-1 390 nm (1 200-1 600 miles;
1 930-2 575 km)
Armament: Pylon under each outer wing for 'Anab'
air-to-air missile, with alternative infra-red or semi-
active radar homing heads
Ordered by: Soviet Air Force

INDEX

INDEX

DRAWINGS:

Roy J. Grainge   11, 17, 23, 29, 33, 35, 37, 39, 41, 47, 51, 53, 65, 67, 71, 75, 77, 83, 85, 99, 105, 107, 121, 129, 131, 137, 139, 141, 147, 165, 167, 171, 173, 177, 179, 195, 205, 207, 209, 211, 213, 215, 217, 219, 221, 227, 237, 245.

Pilot Press   7, 9, 13, 15, 19, 21, 25, 27, 31, 43, 45, 49, 55, 57, 59, 61, 63, 69, 73, 79, 81, 87, 89, 91, 93, 95, 97, 101, 103, 109, 111, 113, 115, 117, 119, 123, 125, 127, 133, 135, 143, 145, 149, 151, 153, 155, 157, 159, 161, 163, 169, 175, 181, 183, 185, 187, 189, 191, 193, 197, 199, 201, 203, 223, 225, 229, 231, 233, 235, 239, 241, 243, 247, 249, 251, 253, 255.

PHOTO CREDITS:

Air Portraits   14, 16, 114
John Blake   216
Canadian Armed Forces   146
French Armed Services   40, 160
Martin Fricke   70, 108
John Fricker   158, 170
Alan W. Hall   124
Denis Hughes   72
B. S. P. Keevill   122
Peter R. March   12
T. Matsuzaki   34, 98, 140, 150
Ministry of Defence   20, 110
Novosti   236
Stephen P. Peltz   64, 76, 90, 176, 220
Planet News   252
The Rev J. D. R. Rawlings   206
Royal Air Force   238
Royal Navy   86, 232, 240
Royal Netherlands Air Force   136
Royal Netherlands Navy   138
Brian M. Service   42, 58, 180
K. Sisson   178
Tass   126, 156, 166, 168, 222, 224, 226, 228, 234, 254
U.S. Navy   74
Venezuelan Air Force   68
Gordon S. Williams   32, 174